The Best of
Alex
1998-2001

Charles Peattie
&
Russell Taylor

Masterley Publishing

The Best of
Alex
1998-2001

We would like to thank FTSE and Mondo Visione
for supporting this book.

FTSE is a world-leader in the creation and management of
global equity indices. We are delighted to be associated with
the Alex cartoon book and hope it brings pleasure
to all those that read it.
www.ftse.com

Mondo Visione, publisher of the Handbook of World Stock, Derivative
and Commodity Exchanges and the Exchange News Direct service, is
pleased to be associated with this collection of the best of Alex - our peer
in global view, savoir faire and impeccable inside information.

For the latest news, visit us at www.exchange-handbook.com

1998

Alex PEATTIE + TAYLOR

BUT, ALEX, NO-ONE GIVES ME ANY <u>WORK</u> TO DO... THAT'S BECAUSE YOU'RE A GRADUATE TRAINEE AND YOU DON'T KNOW HOW TO <u>DO</u> ANYTHING.

I JUST SIT HERE TWIDDLING MY THUMBS AND GAZING INTO SPACE ALL DAY. IF ANYONE TALKS TO ME AT ALL IT'S JUST TO AWARD ME SOME DULL DEMEANING AND USELESS TASK.

I SEE...

SO YOU'D LIKE ME TO ASSIGN YOU A ROLE THAT MAKES YOU FEEL MORE LIKE A PROPER BUSINESS EXECUTIVE?

YES PLEASE.

THE GRADUATE TRAINEE SEEMS HAPPIER...

I TOLD HIM TO IMAGINE HE'S BEING CONSTRUCTIVELY DISMISSED...

Alex PEATTIE + TAYLOR

THESE DAYS ALL GRADUATES' C.V.s HAVE THE OBLIGATORY STRAIGHT A's AT SCHOOL, ONE -SOMETIMES TWO- UNIVERSITY DEGREES...

BUT ACADEMIA IS NOT THE BE-ALL-AND -END-ALL. WE WOULD NOT WANT TO EMPLOY SOME SAD WORKAHOLIC WHO WOULD HAVE NO LIFE AWAY FROM THE OFFICE...

NATURALLY NOT...

WHICH IS WHY ONE LOOKS FOR EVIDENCE IN A RESUMÉ OF A WELL-ROUNDED INDIVIDUAL...ONE WHO HAS PLENTY OF OUTSIDE HOBBIES AND INTERESTS...

YES..

WHICH WE CAN SCREW UP FOR HIM BY GIVING HIM AN URGENT REPORT TO WRITE AT 6.30 PM...

SO WHAT ARE YOU MISSING TONIGHT, PETERS? 5-A-SIDE FOOTBALL OR CHESS CLUB?

email: alex-cartoon@etgate.co.uk

Alex PEATTIE + TAYLOR

FULL IMPLEMENTATION OF OUR MERGER WITH METROBANK HAS BEEN SLIGHTLY DELAYED DUE TO MISUNDERSTANDINGS OVER JOB TITLES...

WE'D FORGOTTEN THAT THEY HAVE A DIFFERENT SYSTEM OF NOMENCLATURE, WHICH INITIALLY CAUSED SOME CONFUSION AMONG THEIR SENIOR PEOPLE WE ARE OFFERING POSTS TO...

FOR EXAMPLE THEIR HEAD OF SALES WAS UNCERTAIN WHETHER HIS NEW ROLE WAS COMMENSURATE WITH HIS EXPERIENCE AND SENIORITY...

SO YOU HAD TO EXPLAIN THAT "RESEARCH ASSOCIATE" IS ROUGHLY EQUIVALENT TO GRADUATE TRAINEE?

AT WHICH POINT HE RESIGNED IN A FIT OF PIQUE AS PLANNED.

email: alex-cartoon@etgate.co.uk

Alex PEATTIE + TAYLOR

ER, ALEX...I COULDN'T HELP WONDERING WHAT'S HAPPENED TO MY DEPARTMENT...

COFF COFF...

THEY WERE ALL SACKED FIRST THING THIS MORNING...

STANDARD CITY PRACTICE. WE GET RID OF PEOPLE WHO DON'T MAKE US MONEY AND ONLY RETAIN THOSE LIKE YOURSELF WHO MAKE A POSITIVE CONTRIBUTION TO THE BANK'S PROFITABILITY...

I DO?

BUT I'M JUST THE GRADUATE TRAINEE...I DON'T DO MUCH MORE THAN KEEP MY PEOPLE SUPPLIED WITH COFFEE AND BRING THEM THEIR NEWSPAPERS AND MAIL...

EXACTLY...

I WANT HALF-DRUNK CUPS OF COFFEE, OPEN PAPERS AND REPORTS TO BE STREWN ACROSS EVERY DESK AND RE-ARRANGED AT HALF-HOURLY INTERVALS SO ANY VISITING CLIENTS DON'T SUSPECT...

email: alex-cartoon@etgate.co.uk

Alex PEATTIE + TAYLOR

MICHELLE, HAVE YOU FINISHED THAT URGENT PHOTOCOPYING I ASKED YOU TO DO?

FLASH!

JUST DOING THE LAST PAGE NOW...

I DON'T KNOW WHY YOU COULDN'T GET YOUR JUNIOR TO DO IT FOR YOU...

ORDINARILY I WOULD ...UNFORTUNATELY THE BORING LITTLE CREEP IS DEEMED TERRIBLY GRAND THESE DAYS...

SO MUCH SO, THAT HE'S ACTUALLY BEING ALLOWED TO ACCOMPANY ME ON A CLIENT VISIT TO NEW YORK TOMORROW... AND FLYING BUSINESS CLASS TOO...

FINISHED...

...AND HERE'S YOUR ORIGINAL BACK...

AH THANKS...

JOHN GRISHAM

NOW, SIMMONDS, KINDLY DON'T DISTURB ME FOR THE NEXT EIGHT HOURS AS I'VE GOT SOME URGENT REPORTS TO READ...

email: alex-cartoon@etgate.co.uk

Alex PEATTIE + TAYLOR

AN EDUCATION AT OXFORD UNIVERSITY IS RIGHTLY FAMED BUT DOES IT REALLY TEACH YOU THE SKILLS THAT EQUIP YOU FOR LIFE?

ONE CARRIES WITH ONE THE TRAPPINGS OF PRIVILEGE THAT COME FROM HAVING ATTENDED THAT AUGUST ALMA MATER, BUT DO THEY BENEFIT ONE IN THE END...?

IN THEORY THEY WILL OPEN DOORS AND GRANT ONE ACCESS TO IMPORTANT PLACES, BUT IS IT ALWAYS LIKE THAT? I SOMETIMES WISH I'D LEARNED SOMETHING PRACTICAL...

SNAP

LIKE HOW TO USE MY STUPID OXFORD UNIVERSITY CREDIT CARD TO SLIP A LOCK...

JUST TRY NOT LOSING YOUR HOUSE KEYS NEXT TIME, CLIVE.

email: alex-cartoon@etgate.co.uk

Alex PEATTIE + TAYLOR

OF COURSE THIS IS A PRELIMINARY PART OF A HEADHUNTER'S WORK WHEN WANTING TO DISCREETLY CHECK OUT A POTENTIAL CANDIDATE.

OH... GOOD AFTERNOON...

DO YOU KNOW A CHAP CALLED ALEX MASTERLEY AT MEGABANK?... OH, I SEE... WELL, NOT TO WORRY... THANKS ANYWAY...

WE'VE HAD NO LUCK SO FAR WITH THIS CHAP...

CLICK

FRANKLY IT LOOKS UNLIKELY WE'LL BE ABLE TO MAKE ANY PROGRESS WITH HIM.

HELLO...DO YOU KNOW ALEX MASTERLEY AT MEGABANK?... REALLY?... OH, EXCELLENT, SPLENDID,

HOLD ON THOUGH. AT LAST...

...A MAITRE D' WHO DOESN'T KNOW HIM...

...IN THAT CASE I'D LIKE TO BOOK A TABLE FOR TWO...

email: alex-cartoon@etgate.co.uk

Alex PEATTIE + TAYLOR

BONJOUR... JE M'APPELLE MONSIEUR DUPONT...

BONJOUR... JE M'APPELLE MONSIEUR DUPONT...

JE SUIS FRANCAIS.

JE SUIS FRANCAIS

REALLY, ALEX. I DON'T KNOW WHY YOU'RE BOTHERING TO LEARN FRENCH FOR OUR HOLIDAY THIS SUMMER...

AUDIO FRENCH

JE SUIS PROFESSEUR

JE SUIS PROFESSEUR

IT'S NOT GOING TO DO YOU ANY GOOD. FRANKLY YOUR ACCENT IS TERRIBLE.

J'ADORE LE SPORT...

THEY'RE NEVER GOING TO BELIEVE YOU'RE THE GENUINE FRENCH HOLDER OF THOSE WORLD CUP TICKETS...

CAN I HELP IT IF I COULD ONLY GET THAT DODGY BATCH OFF A TOUT?

email: alex-cartoon@etgate.co.uk

Strip 1

Alex PEATTIE + TAYLOR

NOW THAT SO MUCH OF OUR WORK IS P.C. BASED, E-MAIL HAS COME AS A REAL BOON...

TAP TAP

FOR EXAMPLE IT CAN GREATLY SPEED UP THE EFFICIENCY OF TAKING STANDARD BUSINESS DECISIONS TO DO WITH THE RUNNING OF THE DEPARTMENT.

THESE DAYS ONE CAN SIMPLY FLASH AN INSTANTANEOUS ELECTRONIC MESSAGE SIMULTANEOUSLY TO ALL PERSONNEL WHICH REQUESTS AN URGENT RESPONSE...

AND THEN SACK THE FIRST FIVE THAT DO.

QUITE. WHEN ONE IS IMPLEMENTING HEADCOUNT REDUCTION IT'S A HANDY WAY TO GAUGE WHO'S NOT GOT ENOUGH WORK TO DO...

email: alex-cartoon@etgate.co.uk

Strip 2

Alex PEATTIE + TAYLOR

DID YOU HEAR ABOUT THIS RADICAL NEW ROAD SCHEME THEY'VE INTRODUCED UP IN LEEDS?

TO ENCOURAGE ENVIRONMENTALLY-FRIENDLY CAR-SHARING THEY'VE CREATED SPECIAL TRAFFIC LANES WHICH SINGLE-OCCUPANCY CARS ARE PROHIBITED FROM USING...

SENSIBLE IDEA...

IT'S GOOD TO KNOW THAT THERE IS A CITY COUNCIL THAT'S TAKING A RESPONSIBLE ATTITUDE TO ROAD CONGESTION AND TRYING TO ENCOURAGE THE RIGHT SORT OF MOTORIST...

GHASTLY PROVINCIAL DUMP... THANK GOODNESS IT'S QUICK TO GET OUT OF THESE DAYS, EH, PERKS?

ZOOOM

LEEDS

email: alex-cartoon@e-gate.co.uk

Strip 3

Alex PEATTIE + TAYLOR

THESE ALL-GLASS MEETING ROOMS ARE A PRACTICAL MEASURE TO PREVENT SEXUAL HARASSMENT.

OBVIOUSLY THEY MAKE IT HARDER FOR AN EMPLOYEE TO HARASS ANOTHER IF HE WOULD BE UNDER OBSERVATION FROM THE WHOLE OFFICE. AT THE SAME TIME THEY HAVE OTHER BENEFITS...

THEY PROMOTE A TYPE OF OPENNESS IN THE DEPARTMENT, NOTHING IS HIDDEN FROM VIEW, EVERYONE CAN SEE WHO IS TALKING TO WHO... IT HELPS FOSTER A CONSTRUCTIVE ATMOSPHERE...

ONE OF RUMOUR, COUNTER-RUMOUR, WILD SPECULATION, FEAR AND MISTRUST...?

QUITE. MAKING THEM ALL PARANOID HELPS KEEP THEM IN LINE...

I EXPECT THEY'RE ALL WONDERING WHAT WE'RE TALKING ABOUT...

email: alex-cartoon@e-gate.co.uk

Strip 4

Alex PEATTIE + TAYLOR

CLIVE...WE'RE LEAVING, WE CAN'T DO BUSINESS WITH THIS LAW FIRM.

EH? BUT WE'VE ONLY JUST ARRIVED...

RECEP

CALL ME OLD-FASHIONED BUT I STILL BELIEVE IN JUDGING PROFESSIONAL PEOPLE BY HOW THEY DRESS AND SARTORIAL STANDARDS ARE NOT UP TO SCRATCH IN THIS PLACE...

YES...

BUT ALEX YOU HAVEN'T SEEN ANYBODY YET. YOU'VE JUST BEEN TO THE LOO... YET YOU CLAIM TO KNOW WHAT'S WORN IN THE BUILDING?

THE BRUSHES ON THE BROWN SHOE BUFFER IN THERE. THEY'RE DECIDEDLY WORN

OH MY GOD...IN OUR BANK ONLY THE BLACK ONE WOULD SHOW ANY SIGN OF USE... LET'S GET OUT OF HERE...

email: alex-cartoon@etgate.co.uk

14

Alex PEATTIE + TAYLOR

THE OFFICE PERSONAL COMPUTER REALLY HAS BECOME A SOPHISTICATED MULTI-FUNCTIONAL TOOL THESE DAYS...

DID YOU KNOW THAT YOU CAN GET DIGITAL STILL CAMERAS THAT CAN DOWNLOAD THE IMAGES THEY TAKE DIRECTLY ONTO THE HARD DISK OF A COMPUTER...

THEN ONE'S GOT ALL THE RESOURCES OF E-MAIL AND SO FORTH...

THAT'S ALL VERY WELL FOR SOME BUT I'M MUCH MORE COMFORTABLE WITH THE SIMPLE TRADITIONAL P.C.

AH, YES...

THE CARDBOARD ONES WITH STANDARD VIEWS THAT THE LESS TECHNOLOGICALLY ADVANCED PEOPLE SEND BACK FROM THEIR HOLIDAYS?...

HERE'S ANOTHER SHOT OF ALEX'S PRIVATE VILLA IN UMBRIA TAKEN 5 MINUTES AGO...

email: alex-cartoon@etgate.co.uk

Alex PEATTIE + TAYLOR

DID YOU HAVE A PLEASANT AND RESTFUL HOLIDAY IN FRANCE, ALEX?

WELL, I FIND I CAN NEVER TOTALLY RELAX WHEN I'M AWAY, CLIVE...

YOU KNOW WHAT IT'S LIKE - ONE'S ALWAYS GOT HALF A MIND ON WHAT WOULD BE GOING ON BACK IN THE CITY... OBVIOUSLY ONE TRIES NOT TO LET ONE'S WIFE KNOW.

RIGHT...

...SHE'D ONLY GET ANNOYED OR WORRIED.

SOMEHOW ONE CAN NEVER JUST LOSE ONESELF, SITTING BACK SIPPING A MID-MORNING GLASS OF CHARDONNAY...

NO...

ONE'S ALWAYS MINDFUL OF THE NEED TO PRETEND ONE'S NOT USED TO IT.

IF SHE HAD ANY IDEA HOW MUCH WE DRINK IN THE COURSE OF A NORMAL WORKING DAY...

WINE BAR

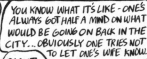

email: alex-cartoon@etgate.co.uk

Alex PEATTIE + TAYLOR

SOMETIMES I FEEL BAD ABOUT THE WAY WE USE OUR GRADUATE TRAINEE AS A DOGSBODY...

YES, ME TOO...

C1 BANK

WHILE WE WENT TO THAT TOP-LEVEL MEETING WE LEFT HIM ASSIGNED TO A MENIAL DUTY WITH NO RELEVANCE TO HIS JOB

IT'S NOT SOMETHING I'M HAPPY ABOUT EITHER...

THERE'S A DANGER HE MIGHT GET A FALSE IDEA ABOUT WHAT HIS LIFE IN THE CITY WILL BE LIKE...

I THINK YOU SHOULD TELL HIM THINGS WON'T ALWAYS BE LIKE THAT...

WINE BAR

I'VE BEEN HERE SINCE LUNCHTIME SAVING YOUR PLACES FOR YOU AS INSTRUCTED...

BY THE WAY, THIS IS THE LAST TIME I GIVE YOU ANY TASK YOU'LL ENJOY...

FRANCE '98

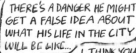
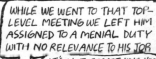

email: alex-cartoon@etgate.co.uk

Alex PEATTIE + TAYLOR

OH, ADAMS... CLIVE AND I HAVE GOT A LUNCHTIME MEETING. COULD YOU BRING IN A BIG ROUND OF SANDWICHES IN ABOUT AN HOUR?

OKAY

OBVIOUSLY IT'S A BIT OF A NUISANCE HAVING TO WORK WHEN WE'D NORMALLY BE IN A RESTAURANT BUT OFTEN THIS CAN BE THE ONLY CONVENIENT TIME FOR ALL PARTIES...

WHEN ONE'S HOLDING A MEETING WITH ONE'S COLLEAGUES, I ALWAYS THINK IT'S A NICE GESTURE TO PROVIDE A DECENT BIG LUNCH FOR EVERYONE IN THE ROOM...

YES...

RUB IT IN TO THE PEOPLE IN JAPAN AND THE U.S. WHAT A CIVILISED TIME OF DAY IT IS OVER HERE IN LONDON.

IT'S 10PM IN TOKYO, 7 AM IN NEW YORK... LET'S HOPE THEY'RE NOT TOO BLEARY TO APPRECIATE IT...

VIDEO CONFERENCING SUITE

email: alex-cartoon@etgate.co.uk

19

Alex PEATTIE + TAYLOR

WHAT'S THIS, CLIVE? YOU'RE SETTING UP A RESTAURANT?

THAT'S RIGHT. WE OPEN NEXT WEEK...

IT'S JUST A LITTLE SIDELINE BUSINESS I INVESTED LAST YEAR'S BONUS IN. I PREDICT IT'LL BECOME A PREMIER EATING VENUE IN THE CITY...

I HOPE THAT YOU'LL VISIT IT IN A PERSONAL CAPACITY AND THAT ALSO YOU'LL WANT TO MAKE IT A PLACE WHERE YOU DO SOME OF YOUR BUSINESS ENTERTAINING.

I'M SURE IT WILL, CLIVE.

TOTALLY DESERTED 365 DAYS A YEAR...NO CHANCE OF MEETING ANYONE I KNOW... SOUNDS THE PERFECT SPOT TO LUNCH WITH MY HEADHUNTER...

Alex PEATTIE + TAYLOR

LOOK, I'M INTERVIEWING YOU FOR A POSITION IN MY RESTAURANT AND WILL ASK YOU ANY QUESTIONS I DEEM RELEVANT...

YES, BUT ALL THESE PERSONAL DETAILS YOU'RE QUIZZING ME ON: OUTSIDE INTERESTS, SOCIAL LIFE, RECREATIONS...IT THAT REALLY NECESSARY?

I'LL BE THE JUDGE OF THAT.

I EXPECT THE VERY HIGHEST STANDARDS FROM MY STAFF AND TO ENSURE YOU HAVE THE APPROPRIATE SKILLS I NEED TO ASK THESE QUESTIONS... NOW, IF I MAY CONTINUE...

WHERE DID I SKI THIS YEAR?

ER... ST ANTON..?

NO, MERIBEL... COME ON, IF YOU WANT TO BE MY MAITRE D' YOU HAVE TO KNOW ME REALLY WELL TO IMPRESS MY FRIENDS...

Alex PEATTIE + TAYLOR

I SEE CLIVE'S TAKEN MR HARDCASTLE TO HIS NEW RESTAURANT FOR LUNCH...

HMMM... YES.

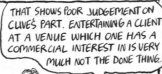

THAT SHOWS POOR JUDGEMENT ON CLIVE'S PART. ENTERTAINING A CLIENT AT A VENUE WHICH ONE HAS A COMMERCIAL INTEREST IN IS VERY MUCH NOT THE DONE THING.

MERCHANT BANKERS ARE EXPECTED TO RETAIN A CERTAIN DIGNITY AND DETACHMENT. THAT SORT OF CRASS BEHAVIOUR CAN ONLY LEAD TO A DIMINISHING OF THE CLIENT'S PROFESSIONAL RESPECT FOR CLIVE...

AND YOU PRESUME TO TELL ME HOW TO RUN MY BUSINESS? THIS FORK'S DIRTY... THERE'S A STAIN ON THE TABLE CLOTH... THE SERVICE IS SLACK...

CHEZ CLIVE

Alex PEATTIE + TAYLOR

I SAID I'D DROP IN AND SEE CLIVE AT THE NEW RESTAURANT HE'S OPENED... AH! THAT'S IT OVER THERE.

CHEZ CLIVE

AH, YES... CLIVE SAID IT HAD A VERY EIGHTIES FEEL. DOESN'T IT TAKE YOU BACK TO THOSE HEADY DAYS OF POWER BREAKFASTS, POWER LUNCHES AND POWER DINNERS DISCUSSING MEGA DEALS?

MENU

...THE THATCHERITE BOOM YEARS WHEN WE WORKED HARD AND PLAYED HARD AND MONEY WAS ABSOLUTELY NO OBJECT. SIGH

ER...BUT, ALEX...THE PLACE IS PRACTICALLY DESERTED...

QUITE...REMINDS ME OF WHEN WE USED TO BOOK ALL THE ADJOINING TABLES SO OUR CONFIDENTIAL BUSINESS DISCUSSIONS WOULDN'T BE OVERHEARD...

QUICK...LET'S SCARPER BEFORE HE SEES US...

email: alex-cartoon@etgate.co.uk

Alex PEATTIE + TAYLOR

WELL, RUPERT, PEOPLE ARE SAYING THAT RUSSIA'S MARKET REFORMS ARE NOW BURNT OUT AND THE COUNTRY'S ECONOMIC COLLAPSE COULD EVEN TRIGGER A GLOBAL RECESSION.

IN VIEW OF WHICH, I IMAGINE WE'LL BE PULLING OUR PEOPLE OUT OF THE RUSSIAN OFFICE...

QUITE THE REVERSE, CLIVE - WE INTEND TO INCREASE PERSONNEL LEVELS OVER IN MOSCOW

AH, SO YOU SEE THIS AS A POSITIVE OPPORTUNITY FOR LONG-TERM INVESTMENT - A CHANCE TO RESTORE WORLDWIDE CONFIDENCE BY FIRM COMMITMENT TO THE RUSSIAN MARKETS?

ER... NO. BUT HOPEFULLY SOME OF THE PEOPLE WE TRANSFER THERE WILL RESIGN AND SAVE US A FEW BOB ON REDUNDANCY PACKAGES ONCE THE BLOOD-LETTING STARTS OVER HERE.

PING

Alex PEATTIE + TAYLOR

THERE'S A RUMOUR GOING ROUND THAT ONE OF OUR TRADERS LOST £100m ON EXPOSURE TO THE RUSSIAN MARKETS...

SOME GREEDY SHORT-TERMIST PUNTING THE BANK'S MONEY ON DODGY RUSSIAN BONDS JUST TO MAXIMISE HIS OWN BOOK PROFIT... BASICALLY HE'S BLOWN OUR BONUSES...

IT'S INFURIATING, CLIVE...

email: alex-cartoon@etgate.co.uk

BUT IN MITIGATION I MUST SAY I HONESTLY BELIEVE HE TOOK A LONG-TERM VIEW ON RUSSIA'S CONTINUED PROFITABILITY AND ACTED CONSISTENTLY, IF SOMEWHAT NAIVELY, IN ACCORDANCE WITH THAT BELIEF...

YOU MEAN HE MIGHT HAVE INVESTED HIS OWN MONEY IN THOSE WORTHLESS GKO BONDS TOO?

YEAH... LET'S HOPE THE IDIOT'S BLOWN HIS SAVINGS AS WELL AS HIS JOB...

Alex PEATTIE + TAYLOR

SO, RUPERT, YOU'RE CONTINUING THE BANK'S CYNICAL POLICY OF TRANSFERRING STAFF TO THE MOSCOW OFFICE IN THE HOPE IT WILL MAKE THEM RESIGN?

LOOK, CLIVE, IT'S THE CRISIS IN RUSSIA THAT'S THREATENING US IN THE WEST WITH RECESSION. WE'VE GOT TO LOOK AT ALL AVAILABLE COST-SAVING OPTIONS...

FOR EXAMPLE IT SEEMS A SENSIBLE IDEA TO DISCONTINUE THE PREFERENTIAL LIMOUSINE SERVICE WE ACCORD TO EXECUTIVES OUT THERE. AFTER ALL THEY CAN ALWAYS TAKE A TAXI FROM MOSCOW AIRPORT...

AND END UP IN A FIELD SOMEWHERE, MUGGED AND STRIPPED OF THEIR CLOTHES AND BELONGINGS?

DO YOU THINK OUR KEY PERSON INSURANCE PAYS OUT IF THEY NEVER MAKE IT TO THEIR HOTEL?

email: alex-cartoon@etgate.co.uk

Alex PEATTIE + TAYLOR

SO HOW'S YOUR RESTAURANT FARING, CLIVE?

TEETERING ON THE BRINK OF BANKRUPTCY, I'M AFRAID, ALEX.

WE'VE JUST REACHED THAT ALL-IMPORTANT POINT - THE END OF OUR FIRST MONTH'S TRADING. OUR FATE IS NO LONGER IN MY OWN HANDS...

EVEN AS WE SPEAK, COSTS RELATING TO THE RESTAURANT ARE BEING CLOSELY EXAMINED AND THE FINANCIAL DECISION WILL SOON BE TAKEN THAT DETERMINES IF WE STAY AFLOAT OR GO UNDER...

AH YES...

email: alex-cartoon@etgate.co.uk

...YOU'VE JUST SUBMITTED YOUR MONTHLY EXPENSES TO RUPERT...

I'M JUST PRAYING HE DOESN'T DISALLOW THEM...

SADLY YOU HAVE BEEN PRACTICALLY THE RESTAURANT'S ONLY CUSTOMER SO FAR...

Strip 1

I.T. PEOPLE REALLY HAVE MADE THEMSELVES INDISPENSIBLE TO A MODERN ORGANISATION... IT'S SOMETHING THAT SENIOR EXECUTIVES OFTEN FAIL TO COMPREHEND.

OVER RECENT YEARS THE INTERNET HAS BECOME A POWERFUL GLOBAL MEDIUM - A VITAL PLATFORM FOR INFORMATION EXCHANGE AND, INCREASINGLY, BUSINESS TRANSACTIONS WITH CLIENTS... NOT THAT THIS MEANS ANYTHING TO RUPERT...

BEING UNABLE EVEN TO SWITCH ON HIS COMPUTER SCREEN HE'S NOT IN A POSITION TO APPRECIATE THE EFFECT THE I.T. STAFF'S WORK CAN HAVE ON THE BANK'S INTERNATIONAL PRESTIGE... NO...

SO, WHO'S GOING TO TELL HIM THAT ONE OF THE BOFFINS HE UNWISELY SACKED YESTERDAY HAS TURNED OUR WEBSITE INTO A HARD CORE PORN PAGE IN REVENGE? BAGSY NOT ME... WWW MEGABANK COM.

email: alex-cartoon@etgate.co.uk

Strip 2

SO YOU WORK IN THE CITY, DO YOU? TELL US ALL ABOUT THIS DISASTROUS SITUATION IN RUSSIA...

ARE YOU ABLE TO SAY? YOUR BANK'S PROBABLY PRETTY INVOLVED IN IT ALL... WELL, THERE IS A DIFFERENCE BETWEEN WHAT I MAY DIVULGE TO A STRANGER AT A DINNER PARTY AS OPPOSED TO A COLLEAGUE AT WORK...

AS A RESULT, WHEN ASKED TO DISCUSS THE BANK'S DEALINGS VIS A VIS RUSSIA I FREQUENTLY HAVE TO OFFER A POLITE BRUSH-OFF AND POINT OUT THAT I AM UNABLE TO COMMENT ON THAT ISSUE. LIKE NOW, WHEN YOU'RE AWAY FROM YOUR BANK?

ER...NO, LIKE WHEN I'M _AT THE_ BANK. THE STANDARD LINE IS: "RUSSIA? SORRY, WASN'T REALLY MY FIELD... I'M MORE ON THE U.K. SIDE." I DON'T WANT TO BLOW MY CHANCE OF GETTING A BONUS THIS YEAR.

email: alex-cartoon@etgate.co.uk

Strip 3

OH MY GOD... MONEY-BROKERS... THERE GOES OUR REPUTATION... A BOTTLE OF YOUR BEST KRUG AND KEEP THEM COMING, MATE... CHEZ CLIVE

LOOK, THIS ISN'T A WINE BAR, IT'S A HIGH-CLASS FRENCH RESTAURANT. I CAN'T SERVE YOU ALCOHOL UNLESS YOU EAT AS WELL... ALL RIGHT... GIVE US A PLATE OF ONION RINGS THEN.

ONION RINGS?! I'VE GOT A MICHELIN-RATED CHEF BACK THERE... WHAT ABOUT THE SOUPE DE JOUR, ENTREES, PLATS CHAUDS, DESSERTS...? IS THERE NO-ONE WHO APPRECIATES _FOOD_? OH... ER... YEAH...

OUR BOSS WHEN HE SIGNS OFF THESE EXPENSES... YEAH... CAN YOU MAKE SURE ALL THAT STUFF APPEARS INSTEAD OF BOOZE ON THE ITEMISED BILL... CHEERS, MATE...

email: alex-cartoon@etgate.co.uk

Strip 4

ANOTHER DISASTROUS NIGHT ...WELL, THAT'S IT... I GAVE IT MY BEST SHOT, BUT WE'LL HAVE TO CLOSE NEXT WEEK...

IN A WAY I'M RELIEVED. WHEN I THINK OF THE PRETENCE, THE INSINCERITY, THE FACADE I'VE HAD TO PUT ON NIGHT AFTER NIGHT JUST TO WOO THE GENERAL PUBLIC INTO MY RESTAURANT...

WELL, NOW THAT I DON'T CARE IF THEY COME BACK AND BRING THEIR FRIENDS OR NOT I CAN FINALLY TELL THE CUSTOMERS WHAT I REALLY THINK OF THEM...

IT'S BEEN A PLEASURE TO SEE YOU... I REALLY AM MOST APPRECIATIVE OF YOUR CUSTOM... OH... ER, THANKS...

YES...HE WAS NEVER CONVINCING AS THE DRUNKEN STROPPY ABUSIVE, HIGHLY-CHARISMATIC RESTAURANTEUR.

email: alex-cartoon@etgate.co.uk

Strip 1

Alex PEATTIE + TAYLOR

I HOPE WE'RE NOT REALLY HEADING FOR ANOTHER RECESSION. IT WILL HAVE SUCH A DEVASTATING EFFECT ON THE PEOPLE I LOOK AFTER...

THEY ALWAYS SEEM TO BE THE FIRST TO SUFFER WHEN THERE'S LESS MONEY AROUND. AND IT'S PEOPLE LIKE ME THEY'RE OBLIGED TO TURN TO FOR HELP...

THEY'RE JUST A BUNCH OF WHINGERS AND SCROUNGERS.

LOOK, YOU AND I TAKE OUR PRIVILEGES FOR GRANTED, BUT IF YOU'D HEARD THE STORIES OF HARDSHIP I LISTEN TO DAILY. THE SHEER DESPERATION OF PEOPLE OFTEN WITH SERIOUS PHYSICAL OR MENTAL DISABILITIES...

...BUT I SUFFER FROM ACUTE CLAUSTROPHOBIA... YOU HAVE TO UPGRADE ME...

I HAVE BUNIONS... I NEED THE EXTRA LEGROOM IN BUSINESS CLASS...

ECONOMY CLASS CHECK IN

OH YES... SOUNDS LIKE THE BANKS HAVE DOWNGRADED THEIR TRAVEL BUDGETS...

email: alex-cartoon@etgate.co.uk

Strip 2

Alex PEATTIE + TAYLOR

GETTING OUR ANALYSTS TO POST THEIR REPORTS ON THE BANK'S INTERNET SITE WAS A SPLENDID INNOVATION...

SO UP TO DATE AND SCIENTIFIC... AND MUCH MORE ECONOMICAL THAN PRINTING OUT HARD COPIES THEN FAXING OR BIKING THEM OVER INDIVIDUALLY TO EACH CLIENT...

THIS WAY, ANY CUSTOMER WORLD-WIDE CAN JUST DIAL UP AND VIEW THE INFO DIRECTLY...

AND IN THESE TIMES OF CUT-BACKS, ALL THIS HAS OBVIOUS COST-SAVING IMPLICATIONS TO THE BANK.

ACCORDING TO THE I.T. PEOPLE, OUR TRAVEL ANALYST'S PAGE HAS HAD ZERO "HITS"...

EXCELLENT... I ALWAYS SUSPECTED NO-ONE READ HIS STUFF... ADD HIM TO THE REDUNDANCY LIST...

email: alex-cartoon@etgate.co.uk

Strip 3

Alex PEATTIE + TAYLOR

RUMOURS ARE SHOOTING ROUND THE BANK THAT XMAS BONUSES ARE GOING TO BE SMALL AND FURTHER CUTBACKS ARE IN THE PIPELINE...

ALL THIS CAN SO EASILY CREATE A MOOD OF UNCERTAINTY AND PARANOIA, WHERE DEVIOUSNESS, PLOTTING, BACKSTABBING AND BEHIND-THE-SCENES MACHINATIONS ABOUND...

WHICH IS WHY I'M GLAD THAT THESE DAYS WE HAVE OPEN-PLAN DEPARTMENTS AND GLASS-WALLED CONFERENCE ROOMS INSTEAD OF THE OLD-STYLE MAZE OF INDIVIDUAL CLOSED-OFF OFFICES...

IT'S MUCH BETTER, I AGREE...

I MEAN, MYERS IS BOUND TO NOTICE HE'S THE ONLY PERSON WHO HASN'T BEEN INVITED TO THIS MEETING...

LET'S HOPE HE GETS THE HINT AND RESIGNS, EH?

email: alex-cartoon@etgate.co.uk

Strip 4

Alex PEATTIE + TAYLOR

ALEX, THESE DAYS YOU GET BACK FROM WORK AND HEAD STRAIGHT FOR THE DRINKS CABINET. IT'S NOT LIKE YOU...

THINGS ARE BAD IN THE CITY, PENNY. IT'S BEEN A TERRIBLE QUARTER FOR BANKS. THERE ARE RUMOURS OF LARGE-SCALE CUTBACKS WHICH MAY EXTEND TO JOB LOSSES AND NON-PAYMENT OF BONUSES...

ALEX, DON'T PLEASE...

I CAN'T BEAR TO SEE YOU DRINKING LIKE THIS... YOU'RE POLISHING OFF SEVERAL LARGE SCOTCHES EVERY EVENING... I'M STARTING TO GET SERIOUSLY WORRIED.

NORMALLY YOU'D NOW BE "ON THE WAGON" FOR A MONTH IN PREPARATION FOR ALL THE XMAS PARTY EXCESSES...

LET'S FACE IT, PENNY THERE AREN'T GOING TO BE ANY THIS YEAR...

email: alex-cartoon@etgate.co.uk

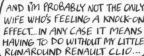

27

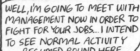

Strip 1:

THANK YOU FOR ELECTING ME AS YOUR DEPARTMENTAL REPRESENTATIVE TO THE BANK'S WORKS COUNCIL...

WE'VE ALL LIVED IN STASIS SINCE THE IMPENDING REDUNDANCIES WERE ANNOUNCED. TOP SALESMEN SITTING AROUND, IGNORING THEIR CLIENTS, SWAPPING WORRIED GOSSIP ABOUT THE LATEST RUMOURS...

WELL, I'M GOING TO MEET WITH MANAGEMENT NOW IN ORDER TO FIGHT FOR YOUR JOBS... I INTEND TO SEE NORMAL ACTIVITY RESUMED ROUND HERE...

I SEE BROKERLY ACTIVITY HAS RESUMED... WINING, DINING, ENTERTAINING, GENERALLY LICKING UP...

FANCY COMING TO THE RUGBY? I'VE GOT TICKETS TO "THE BLUE ROOM"

YOU'LL PUT IN A GOOD WORD FOR ME...?

email: alex-cartoon@etgate.co.uk

Strip 2:

WE ARE THE REPRESENTATIVES OF THE WORKS COUNCIL ELECTED BY THE EMPLOYEES OF THIS BANK TO NEGOTIATE THE ANNOUNCED JOB CUTS...

WE INTEND TO PROVIDE A UNITED FRONT TO PROTECT THE INTERESTS OF THE WORKFORCE. SO I HOPE YOU DON'T THINK WE ARE JUST HERE TO RUBBER-STAMP YOUR EXISTING REDUNDANCY LIST...

CERTAINLY NOT. LET ME ASSURE YOU WE ARE MOST FLEXIBLE. NOW, HERE IS THE LIST...

OH, WEBSTER, I THINK YOU'LL NOTICE YOUR NAME'S ON IT...

WHA-AT ?!? ...BUT I SUPPOSE WE COULD TAKE YOU OFF AND PUT HODGKINSON ON INSTEAD...

ME? HOLD ON...

OKAY, MYERS THEN...

WAIT A MINUTE...

email: alex-cartoon@etgate.co.uk

Strip 3:

I STILL DON'T SEE WHY WE'RE INCLUDING THESE EMPLOYEE REPRESENTATIVES IN OUR DELIBERATIONS OVER WHO GETS MADE REDUNDANT...

DON'T FORGET, DAVID, AS MANAGEMENT WE ARE REMOTE FROM OUR WORKFORCE, YET WE ARE TAKING DECISIONS AT A REMOVE WHICH AFFECT THE JOBS OF THESE PEOPLE WE MAY NOT EVEN KNOW PERSONALLY...

THE WORKS COUNCILS ARE THE CONDUIT OF COMMUNICATION WITH OUR EMPLOYEES. WORKING ALONGSIDE THEM ON A DAY-TO-DAY BASIS THEY PROVIDE THAT VITAL LINK WITH THOSE WHOSE FATES ARE AT STAKE...

EXCELLENT. LOOKS LIKE NEWS HAS LEAKED OUT WHO'S ON THE HIT LIST...

OH GOOD. I DO HATE IT WHEN THEY BURST INTO TEARS OF SHOCK IN MY OFFICE.

CUT

email: alex-cartoon@etgate.co.uk

Strip 4:

WHAT ARE YOU COMPLAINING ABOUT, MIKE? AT LEAST YOU'RE ON THE WORKS COUNCIL NEGOTIATING CUT BACKS WITH MANAGEMENT...

THAT MEANS YOUR JOB IS SAFE...

MAYBE. BUT I'M OUT OF THE ACTION. EVERYONE KNOWS THAT FALLING AND HIGHLY VOLATILE MARKETS CREATE MONEY-MAKING OPPORTUNITIES FOR PEOPLE WITH NOUS...

I'M NOT ABLE TO TAKE ADVANTAGE OF THE POTENTIAL BONANZA BECAUSE I'M SPENDING ALL MY TIME IN MEETINGS WITH MANAGEMENT DISCUSSING REDUNDANCIES...

NATURALLY...

WHICH MAKES YOU AN INSIDER.

ALEX. WHAT ODDS ARE YOU MAKING ON THE WHOLE EMERGING MARKETS DIVISION BEING SACKED?

EVENS.

£10 £10

email: alex-cartoon@etgate.co.uk

29

Alex — PEATTIE + TAYLOR

Panel 1: JONATHAN HUGHES HERE. OH, HELLO, ALEX...LUNCH? I'D LOVE TO...TOMORROW? ....I'M PRETTY SURE I'M FREE... I'LL JUST CHECK MY DIARY.

Panel 2: WITH THE DEARTH OF CORPORATE ACTIVITY AT THE MOMENT THERE'S NOT MUCH ELSE FOR US TO DO...HOLD ON...MY SECRETARY'S BOOKED HERSELF IN FOR HER XMAS LUNCH WITH ME TOMORROW...

Panel 3: IT'S HER BIG ANNUAL TREAT... ODD, THOUGH,...IT'S NOT NORMALLY TILL MID-DECEMBER...STILL, TOMORROW MUST BE THE OPTIMUM DAY...SHE'S EXTREMELY GOOD AT HER JOB...

HOW ABOUT THE DAY AFTER?...HELLO?...HELLO?

Panel 4: DID YOU FIX UP LUNCH WITH JONATHAN?

NO POINT. SOUNDS LIKE HE'S ON THE REDUNDANCY LIST AND THE NEWS HAS HIT THE SECRETARIES' GRAPEVINE...

email: alex-cartoon@etgate.co.uk

Alex — PEATTIE + TAYLOR

Panel 1: I HEAR THAT RICHARD BRANSON HAS ISSUED HIS EMPLOYEES WITH HEALTH WARNINGS REGARDING THE USE OF MOBILE PHONES...

Panel 2: HARDLY SURPRISING, CLIVE...AFTER ALL THERE'S INCREASING SPECULATION THAT HOLDING A POWERFUL MICRO-WAVE SOURCE UP TO ONE'S EAR CAN POTENTIALLY DAMAGE THE BRAIN...

Panel 3: ...CAUSING HEADACHES, DIZZINESS, ABSENT-MINDEDNESS... POSSIBLY LEADING TO FULL-SCALE DEMENTIA IN HEAVY USERS. OF COURSE IT'S HARD TO GATHER ANY RELIABLE STATISTICS...

YES...

Panel 4: NOW EVERYONE'S GOT THESE SAFETY-CONSCIOUS EAR-PIECES FOR THEIR PHONES...

THEY ALL LOOK LIKE THEY'RE WANDERING ROUND TALKING TO THEMSELVES... KEEP ME INFORMED.

I'LL BE HOME ABOUT 7...

Alex — PEATTIE + TAYLOR

Panel 1: LOOK, AS YOU ALL KNOW WE NEED TWO PEOPLE TO STAFF THE DESK OVER THE XMAS AND NEW YEAR PERIOD...

XMAS ROTA '98 / XMAS / NEW YEAR

Panel 2: AS WE ARE UNABLE TO AGREE ON WHO SHOULD BE STUCK HERE ON THEIR OWN OVER THE FESTIVE SEASON I'M GOING TO HAVE TO MAKE AN EXECUTIVE DECISION...

XMAS ROTA '98 / XMAS / NEW YEAR

email: alex-cartoon@etgate.co.uk

Panel 3: IT'S NOT FAIR. JUST BECAUSE WE'RE JUNIOR WE GET NO SAY IN THE MATTER AND WE'LL END UP GETTING A RAW DEAL.

THAT'S TOUGH LUCK, VANESSA.

XMAS ROTA '98 / XMAS / NEW YEAR

Panel 4: NOW YOU'VE GOT THE PERFECT EXCUSE FOR NOT DOING IT NEXT YEAR.

NO WAY AM I GOING TO BE AROUND WHEN THAT MILLENNIUM BUG HITS THE FAN.

XMAS ROTA '98 / XMAS Alex Clive / NEW YEAR Alex Clive

Alex — PEATTIE + TAYLOR

Panel 1: ANNA, CAN I REMIND YOU THAT THE BANK IS CURRENTLY IMPLEMENTING A PROGRAMME OF CUTBACKS DUE TO TRADING LOSSES...

Panel 2: WHEN I LEFT YOU IN CHARGE OF ORGANISING THE DEPARTMENTAL XMAS PARTY I EXPECTED THAT EXPENDITURE WOULD REFLECT THIS BELT-TIGHTENING MOOD...

I'M SORRY, RUPERT...

email: alex-cartoon@etgate.co.uk

Panel 3: IN A YEAR WHEN WE ARE UNABLE TO PAY OUT STAFF BONUSES I WANT TO SEND A CLEAR MESSAGE TO THAT EFFECT VIA A SUITABLY AUSTERE AND RESTRAINED XMAS PARTY...

Panel 4: SO HOW DARE YOU FINANCIALLY DOWNGRADE IT TO EXCLUDE SPOUSES? DO YOU WANT OUR PEOPLE TO HAVE A GOOD TIME?...

REINSTATE THE OTHER HALVES AND LET'S KEEP A MOOD OF MISERY GOING...

Strip 1:

HAWKINS?! WHAT ARE YOU DOING HERE? I SACKED YOU A WEEK AGO....

YES, RUPERT...I'VE COME FOR MY REVENGE

GET THE REST OF THE DEPARTMENT HERE...I'M HOLDING YOU ALL HOSTAGE...

WHAT? YOU CRAZY VICIOUS FOOL! HOW CAN YOU DO THIS TO YOUR OLD COLLEAGUES?

SHUT UP AND DO IT... ER...ALEX...COULD YOU STEP INTO MY OFFICE...BRING THE REST OF THE TEAM WITH YOU...

UTTER TERROR

RELAX, CHAPS. YOU'RE NOT BEING SACKED, JUST HELD HOSTAGE BY A DERANGED GUNMAN...

OH PHEW-EE...YOU REALLY HAD US SPOOKED THERE, RUPERT...

email: alex-cartoon@etgate.co.uk

Strip 2:

HAWKINS YOU'RE HOLDING THE CORPORATE FINANCE TEAM AT GUNPOINT...PLEASE RELEASE A HOSTAGE AS A GOOD FAITH GESTURE...

RUPERT STERLING IS THE OLDEST AND I HAPPEN TO KNOW HE HAS A HEART CONDITION...HE MAY NOT BE ABLE TO LAST OUT THE PRESSURE...

OH...OKAY...

OUT YOU GO, OLD MAN...

MR STERLING, ARE YOU ALL RIGHT?

MY GOD...WHAT AN ORDEAL...TRAPPED IN A SITUATION FROM MY WORST NIGHTMARES...HELPLESS...UNABLE TO ESCAPE...

THE GUNMAN'S A TOTAL PSYCHOPATH, EH?

OH NO...HE WAS FINE...IT WAS THE REST OF THEM ALL TAKING THE OPPORTUNITY TO BUTTONHOLE ME ABOUT THEIR BONUS EXPECTATIONS...

email: alex-cartoon@etgate.co.uk

Strip 3:

WHAT'S THE SITUATION, INSPECTOR?

WELL, AS YOU KNOW, MR STERLING, YOU HAVE A DISGRUNTLED EX-EMPLOYEE WHO HAS "GONE POSTAL"...

...HE'S CURRENTLY HOLDING FIVE MEMBERS OF STAFF HOSTAGE AT GUNPOINT IN YOUR OFFICE. WE'RE TRYING TO NEGOTIATE WITH HIM...

SIR, WE'VE GOT HIS WIFE ON THE PHONE

GOOD WORK, SERGEANT. PUT HER THROUGH TO HIM...

SOUND PSYCHOLOGICAL THINKING...SPEAKING TO HER MIGHT HELP PERSUADE HIM TO GIVE HIMSELF UP...

OH, ER...HELLO, DARLING...ER...NO I WON'T BE BACK FOR DINNER TONIGHT...I'VE GOT TO WORK LATE...WE'VE GOT AN URGENT DEAL ON...ER...

SO! HE HASN'T TOLD HER HE'S BEEN SACKED YET...

email: alex-cartoon@etgate.co.uk

Strip 4:

FRANK'S OUR TOP NEGOTIATOR. HE SHOULD BE ABLE TO FREE YOUR EXECUTIVES BEING HELD AT GUNPOINT BY HAWKINS, THEIR EX-COLLEAGUE.

WE'RE WITNESSING A REAL PROFESSIONAL AT WORK HERE...

SOMEONE WHO STRIVES TO BE HELPFUL, CONCILIATORY, ACCOMMODATING, REASSURING, WHILE AT THE SAME TIME TRYING TO IMPOSE HIS WILL ON THE OTHER PARTY BY CHARMING HIS WAY INTO HIS TRUST...

...ALL THE TIME REALISING THAT HE IS DEALING WITH SOMEONE AT THE OTHER END OF THE PHONE WHO IS POTENTIALLY VOLATILE AND COULD HANG UP IF HE FEELS THINGS ARE NOT RIGHT...

OH YES...HE'S GOOD ALL RIGHT...

BUT I WISH HE'D GET OFF THE LINE AND PUT OUR NEGOTIATOR THROUGH TO THE GUNMAN...

ALEX, I AM NOT ONE OF HAWKINS' EX-CLIENTS. PLEASE STOP INGRATIATING YOURSELF WITH ME AND LET ME TALK TO HIM...

IS THIS ABOUT SOMETHING I CAN HELP WITH?

email: alex-cartoon@etgate.co.uk

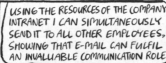

Strip 1:

Alex — PEATTIE + TAYLOR

YOU SENDING ONE OF THOSE E-MAIL CHRISTMAS CARDS, ALEX?

THAT'S RIGHT, CLIVE

USING THE RESOURCES OF THE COMPANY INTRANET I CAN SIMULTANEOUSLY SEND IT TO ALL OTHER EMPLOYEES, SHOWING THAT E-MAIL CAN FULFIL AN INVALUABLE COMMUNICATION ROLE.

INVALUABLE COMMUNICATION ROLE? PURVEYING BLAND SEASONAL WISHES TO EVERYONE IN THE ORGANISATION WORLDWIDE, THE VAST MAJORITY OF WHOM YOU DON'T EVEN KNOW?!

YOU'LL SEE...

AH, LOOK... TWELVE OF THEM HAVE COME STRAIGHT BACK TO ME MARKED "RECIPIENT UNKNOWN" THAT'S A DOZEN SACKINGS TODAY ALREADY.

Strip 2:

Alex — PEATTIE + TAYLOR

THE BARRINGTON HOTEL

HELLO? BARRINGTON HOTEL...

OH, HELLO... I'M CALLING ABOUT YOUR AVAILABILITY FOR CHRISTMAS PARTIES...

I'VE STUPIDLY LEFT EVERYTHING TO THE LAST MINUTE. I'VE BEEN PHONING ROUND EVERY VENUE BUT NO-ONE'S HAD ANY CANCELLATIONS. I DON'T SUPPOSE YOU'VE... ER...?

YOU'RE IN LUCK, SIR... A GENTLEMAN FROM MINERAL BANK JUST CALLED TO CANCEL THEIR PARTY BOOKING...

OH THANK GOODNESS... YOU'VE SAVED MY LIFE...

SO YOU'D LIKE TO BOOK...? HELLO? ... HELLO?...

CLICK BRRRR

SO YOU GOT A STORY JUST IN TIME?

YES. "MINERAL BANK IN SERIOUS FINANCIAL TROUBLE"... I'LL SEE YOU AT OUR XMAS PARTY IN HALF AN HOUR.

DAILY BUGLE CITY DESK

TAP TAP

email: alex-cartoon@etgate.co.uk

Strip 3:

Alex — PEATTIE + TAYLOR

WELL, LUCY, WE'VE DONE MORE BUSINESS THIS LUNCHTIME THAN THE REST OF THE MONTH PUT TOGETHER...

I TOLD YOU WE WOULD, ALAN. TODAY'S THE DAY THE BONUSES AT MEGABANK WERE ANNOUNCED AND CITY MENTALITY IS VERY PREDICTABLE.

SO IT'S VINTAGE KRUG AND CHATEAU LAFITE ALL ROUND... CONSPICUOUS CONSUMPTION TO EXCESS OF EVERY LUXURY ITEM WE STOCK... LOOK AT THAT MOOD. IT'S JUST LIKE THE OLD DAYS...

YEAH...

LIKE 1992... THE LAST TIME THEY ALL GOT ZILCH.

... AND TOOK THEIR FEEBLE REVENGE ON THE BANK BY PUNISHING THE COMPANY PLASTIC.

GLOOM

DESPONDENCY

email: alex-cartoon@etgate.co.uk

Strip 4:

Alex — PEATTIE + TAYLOR

MEGABANK KIDS' XMAS PARTY

SO WHAT DO YOU WANT FOR CHRISTMAS CHRISTOPHER?

A BIKE... A ZIP DRIVE FOR MY P.C. ... TOMB RAIDER III...

WELL YOU'D BETTER GO AND TELL SANTA...

SANTA'S GROTTO →

DON'T BE STUPID, UNCLE CLIVE. PRESENTS DON'T COME FROM SANTA. THEY COME FROM MY DAD...

THAT'S TRUE, CHRISTOPHER, BUT IF YOU WANT YOUR PRESENTS IT WOULD BE A NICE IDEA TO GO AND SEE SANTA WITH THE OTHER KIDS... YOU KNOW WHAT TO ASK HIM, DON'T YOU?

OH... OKAY, DADDY.

SO WHAT'S MY DAD'S BONUS LOOKING LIKE THIS YEAR?

SANTA GROTTO

SNEAKY MOVE – RUPERT VOLUNTEERING TO BE SANTA.

HE HOPED IT WOULD STOP US BEING ABLE TO USE THE PARTY TO BADGER HIM...

email: alex-cartoon@etgate.co.uk

1999

Alex

Strip 1

WELL, ALL OUR SYSTEMS FOR DEALING IN THE EURO ARE UP AND RUNNING... WE IN MANAGEMENT CAN AWARD OURSELVES A PAT ON THE BACK

OF COURSE, TECHNICALLY IT WAS OUR SUBORDINATES WHO PUT IN THE HOURS, WORKED EVENINGS, CAME IN AT WEEKENDS RIGHT THROUGH THE FESTIVE SEASON TO GET EVERYTHING OPERATIONAL IN TIME...

TRUE...

BUT NONE OF THIS WOULD HAVE BEEN POSSIBLE WITHOUT OUR STRATEGIC VISION, OUR POWERS OF DECISION-MAKING, FORWARD PLANNING AND IMPLEMENTATION.

AH YES...

...DELAYING THE ANNOUNCEMENT OF THE XMAS BONUSES TILL TODAY....

NOW WE CAN LET THE GREEDY LITTLE LOSERS KNOW THEY'RE GETTING ZILCH...

Strip 2

WELL, CLIVE, NO SENSE IN STANDING IN LINE IN THE CHECK-IN QUEUE...

HEATHROW DEPARTURES

NOT NOW THAT AIRPORTS HAVE THESE AUTOMATIC CHECK-IN MACHINES WHICH MAKE THE PROCESS OF REGISTERING FOR A FLIGHT A TOTALLY PAINLESS EXPERIENCE...

AUTOMATIC CHECK-IN

IT'S THE PERFECT CONVENIENCE INNOVATION FOR MODERN-DAY EXECUTIVES LIKE YOU AND ME, CONSIDERING THE AMOUNT OF BUSINESS TRAVELLING WE DO...

AUTOMATIC CHECK-IN

YES...

...SO LITTLE THAT WE'VE SHAMINGLY LOST OUR GOLD FREQUENT FLYER CARD STATUS...

BLASTED RECESSION...DO YOU THINK THERE'S AN "UPGRADE" BUTTON ON THIS THING?

GOLD CARD CHECK-IN

Strip 3

LOOK, I KNOW THAT IT MUST BE HARD FOR YOU TO FREE YOURSELF FROM YOUR TRADITIONALIST WAY OF THINKING...

SIR?

AFTER ALL THIS IS A VERY STRAIGHT-LACED OLD-FASHIONED CITY CLUB. BUT I JUST WANT YOU TO KNOW UP-FRONT THAT I AM GAY...

I SEE, SIR...

NOW, THAT DOES NOT MEAN THAT I AM FRIVOLOUS AND PROMISCUOUS. ACTUALLY I'M IN A LONG-TERM RELATIONSHIP – JUST LIKE A MARRIAGE – ONLY IT HAPPENS TO BE WITH A MAN... HIS NAME IS TREVOR...

...SO IF HE CALLS AND ASKS FOR ME, TELL HIM I'M NOT HERE...

THANK YOU, SIR. OBVIOUSLY I'D HAVE AUTOMATICALLY SAID THAT TO ANY LADY CALLER...

Strip 4

LOOK, MR HARDCASTLE, IT'S ALL VERY WELL YOU MOUTHING OFF SELF-RIGHTEOUSLY ABOUT CORPORATE CITIZENSHIP.

HARDCASTLE A.G.M.

...BUT WHAT ABOUT THE CHEMICAL REPROCESSING PLANT YOU OWN OUT IN INDIA WHICH IS PUMPING OUT EFFLUENTS AND POISONING THE ENVIRONMENT..?

AHEM... ER, JUST A MOMENT...

I CAN'T BEGIN TO ANSWER A QUESTION LIKE THAT... YOU'RE MY ADVISER, SO TELL ME: DO WE HAVE A PLANT OUT THERE?...AND, IF SO, WHERE?

OF COURSE WE DO, MR HARDCASTLE.

3RD ROW... THE CHAP ON THE RIGHT IN THE RED TIE...

NEXT QUESTION, PLEASE... YOU, SIR...

WOULD THE CHAIRMAN TELL US ABOUT HIS CHARITY WORK...?

email: alex-cartoon@etgate.co.uk

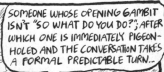

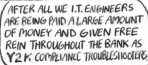

Strip 1:
- **Alex** PEATTIE + TAYLOR: DID YOU KNOW THAT CLIVE'S AN ENTHUSIASTIC CHARITABLE FUND-RAISER? HE'S RUNNING THE LONDON MARATHON THIS YEAR...
- THE MARATHON? I HAD NO IDEA... HE HASN'T MENTIONED IT...
- OH YES. HE'S BEEN GETTING UP EARLY TO DO 5-MILE RUNS EVERY MORNING, GOING TO THE GYM AT LUNCHTIME, THEN MORE HOURS OF ROAD-POUNDING IN THE EVENING... REALLY?
- HOW CONSIDERATE OF YOU TO MENTION IT, ALEX. / WELL, I THOUGHT YOU'D LIKE TO KNOW HOW HARD HE'S BEEN TRAINING. AFTER ALL HE'S PROBABLY HOPING TO GET A GENEROUS AMOUNT OF MONEY FROM YOU...
- AS HIS BONUS? YES IN VIEW OF THIS I WAS PLANNING TO UPGRADE IT... ZZZZ... / NO NEED. HONESTLY, THIS HAS NOTHING TO DO WITH OVERWORK...

email: alex-cartoon@etgate.co.uk

Strip 2:
- TECHNOLOGY HAS REALLY CHANGED THE WAY THE CITY WORKS. WE USED TO SEND OUT ALL OUR BROKER RESEARCH IN HARD COPY BY MAIL.
- THEN WE GRADUATED TO FAXES, AND MORE RECENTLY E-MAIL. NOW OUR FUND MANAGER CLIENTS CAN EVEN USE REUTERS' ON-LINE SERVICE TO READ ALL THE AVAILABLE RESEARCH IN REAL TIME...
- BUT DON'T YOU THINK THAT BY PROVIDING OUR CLIENTS WITH INCREASINGLY SOPHISTICATED ACCESS TO INFORMATION, WE SALES PEOPLE COULD BE PUTTING OURSELVES OUT OF A JOB? / NOT AT ALL... THAT'S A CLIENT PHONING NOW... RING RING / Caller I.D. / RING
- ALL RIGHT... NOW THAT I'M GETTING ALL THIS RUBBISH IN QUADRUPLICATE, WILL SOMEONE KINDLY TELL ME WHAT, IF ANY OF IT, TO READ... / YOU'VE COME TO THE RIGHT PERSON... / YOU HAVE 157 NEW e-mails / REUTERS / FAX

email: alex-cartoon@etgate.co.uk

Strip 3:
- **Alex** PEATTIE + TAYLOR: OH, MIKE, I WAS WONDERING IF YOU'D CARE TO MAKE A CONTRIBUTION TO CHARITY... / WHAT'S THIS, CLIVE? YOU'RE RUNNING IN THE LONDON MARATHON?
- YES. ALL MY WORK COLLEAGUES HAVE SPONSORED ME. PEOPLE JUST PUT DOWN THEIR NAME AND ADDRESS AND WHATEVER AMOUNT THEY CAN AFFORD TO PLEDGE... / WHAT A GOOD IDEA...
- WHAT SORT OF SUM WERE YOU THINKING OF? / OH I DON'T KNOW... HOW ABOUT TWENTY POUNDS? / NO PROBLEM...
- A PHOTOCOPIED UP-TO-DATE STAFF LIST OF YOUR DEPARTMENT WITH HOME ADDRESSES AND AN INDICATION OF CURRENT EARNINGS... THANKS... / I KNEW A HEADHUNTER WOULD BE TOO MERCENARY TO ACTUALLY SPONSOR ME.

email: alex-cartoon@etgate.co.uk

Strip 4:
- **Alex** PEATTIE + TAYLOR: DO YOU KNOW, PENNY, NEXT SATURDAY IS THE IDEAL NIGHT FOR CONCEPTION FOR A BABY TO BE BORN ON JANUARY 1ST 2000?
- OH, ALEX. YOU'VE ALWAYS SAID YOU WEREN'T SURE ABOUT AN ADDITION TO THE FAMILY. ARE YOU REALLY CONTEMPLATING A BABY FOR THE NEW MILLENNIUM?
- I THINK SO, PENNY. OBVIOUSLY I'M KEENLY AWARE OF ALL THE ATTENDANT PROBLEMS AND RESPONSIBILITIES, HOW DISRUPTIVE AND DESTABILISING THE WHOLE THING COULD BE... / HAVING A BABY?
- NO, THE MILLENNIUM. PATERNITY LEAVE SEEMS A USEFUL WAY OF NOT BEING IN THE OFFICE WHEN THE Y2K BUG STRIKES.

email: alex-cartoon@etgate.co.uk

Alex — PEATTIE + TAYLOR

ALEX, RUMOUR HAS REACHED ME THAT YOU AND AMANDA SLEPT TOGETHER ON A BUSINESS TRIP LAST WEEK.

NOT AT ALL, RUPERT. IT WAS A STUPID DRUNKEN ONE-OFF WHICH I HAVE NO INTENTION OF REPEATING...

I SUSPECT THAT THIS KIND OF CASUAL ARRANGEMENT CAME RATHER EASILY TO BOTH OF YOU.

I'M SORRY, ALEX. THIS TOUCHES ON ISSUES ON WHICH THE BANK HAS VERY STRONG PRINCIPLES. I'M AFRAID I HAVE NO CHOICE BUT TO TAKE IMMEDIATE FIRM ACTION.

HE'S MADE ROOM-SHARING COMPULSORY ON ALL BUSINESS TRIPS.

BLASTED COST-CUTTING...

Alex — PEATTIE + TAYLOR

EVER SINCE OUR BLASTED BANK STARTED MAKING US FLY STEERAGE WE'VE HAD TO COME UP WITH RUSES TO GET UPGRADED...

CHECK IN

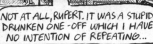

ARRIVING DELIBERATELY LATE IN THE HOPE THAT ECONOMY CLASS IS FULL SO WE'LL GET BUMPED UP TO BUSINESS IS STILL THE BEST PLOY...

ACTUALLY I'VE GOT A SNEAKIER ONE...

A DOCTOR'S CERTIFICATE SAYING THAT DUE TO A SERIOUS BACK PROBLEM I AM UNABLE TO SIT IN CRAMPED CABINS AND NEED THE EXTRA LEGROOM IN CLUB...

LET'S GO.

I'M SORRY, GENTLEMEN, BUT ECONOMY CLASS IS FULL...

SORRY. THE TRAFFIC WAS TERRIBLE.

...SO ARE BUSINESS AND FIRST... BUT I COULD UPGRADE YOU BOTH TO CONCORDE.

I'D BE DELIGHTED... BUT MY COLLEAGUE IS REGRETFULLY UNABLE...

SNATCH

NO...IT'S ALL A MISTAKE.

Alex — PEATTIE + TAYLOR

I'M EXPECTING AN URGENT COMMUNICATION FROM A CLIENT...

Welcome to e-mail.

OF COURSE IN THIS DIGITAL AGE IF YOU WANT TO GET IMMEDIATE ACCESS TO INFORMATION YOU'VE GOT TO KEEP ABREAST OF HOW TECHNOLOGY IS DEVELOPING, CLIVE.

Checking for e-mail.

E-MAIL AND THE INTERNET NOW PROVIDE A READILY-AVAILABLE INSTANTANEOUS DATA TRANSFER FACILITY IN A GLOBAL NETWORK LINKING LITERALLY MILLIONS OF USERS.

You have 86 new e-mails.

TAP.

SO NOWADAYS I TELL MY BEST CLIENTS TO FAX ME SOMETHING IF THEY WANT ME TO ACTUALLY READ IT...

all e-mails deleted

WHIRR, WHIRR

Alex — PEATTIE + TAYLOR

DOESN'T YOUR HEART SINK WHEN YOU COME ACROSS YET ANOTHER PERFECT C.V. FROM A GRADUATE JOB APPLICANT?

STRAIGHT A'S RIGHT THROUGH SCHOOL, FIRST CLASS DEGREE IN APPLIED MATHEMATICS, POST-GRADUATE MBA, HOLIDAYS SPENT WORKING ON A TRADING DESK...

IT'S A WHOLE DIFFERENT GENERATION, CLIVE.

WELL I ALWAYS SAY TO THEM THAT PAPER ACADEMIC QUALIFICATIONS DON'T TELL ME WHETHER A CANDIDATE CAN THINK... AND WORK EXPERIENCE IS NOT NECESSARILY PREFERABLE TO, SAY, TRAVEL WHICH CREATES A ROUNDED INDIVIDUAL...

WISE WORDS TO INSTIL INTO A YOUNG PROSPECTIVE EMPLOYEE...

...TO COVER YOURSELF JUST IN CASE HE EVER COMES ACROSS YOUR WOEFUL C.V.

DEPRESSING TO THINK THAT YOU AND I WOULDN'T EVEN GET A FIRST INTERVIEW THESE DAYS...

email: alex-cartoon@etgate.co.uk

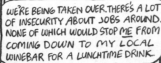

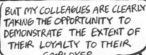

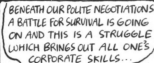

Alex PEATTIE + TAYLOR

I'M SO GLAD YOU'RE MAKING THIS DOCU-MENTARY ABOUT THE CITY BECAUSE THERE ARE CERTAIN ASPECTS THAT PEOPLE DON'T SEE...

FOR EXAMPLE WE HAVE TO GET UP REALLY EARLY. AS YOU SEE, I ARRIVE AT THE STATION BEFORE PEOPLE ARE EVEN OUT OF THEIR BEDS...

DRIVING ALONG THE COUNTRY ROADS AT THIS TIME, JUST THE BIRDS SINGING, NOT A HUMAN SOUL AROUND, IT CAN MAKE YOU QUESTION THE POINT OF OUR MATERIALISTIC LIFESTYLES...

YES...?

YES. LIKE THIS PORSCHE... I MEAN, WHAT'S THE POINT IF NO-ONE'S AROUND TO SEE IT? SOMETIMES I JUST TAKE THE FAMILY RUN-ABOUT...

BY THE WAY DON'T FORGET TO GET A SHOT OF THE PERSONALISED NUMBERPLATES...

Alex PEATTIE + TAYLOR

I'M GLAD WE WERE PICKED TO FEATURE IN THIS FLY-ON-THE-WALL DOCUMENTARY THAT'S CURRENTLY BEING FILMED ABOUT THE CITY...

JUST THINK: WHEN IT'S SHOWN ON THE T.V. MILLIONS OF VIEWERS WILL WATCH IT. IT'LL BE FUNNY TO BE RECOGNISED IN PUBLIC BY ORDINARY PEOPLE...

WHEN THEY SEE ME PASS THEY'LL PROBABLY SAY "OH, YOU'RE CLIVE. YOU WORK AT MEGABANK. I'VE SEEN YOU ON T.V.."

YES INDEED..

...MAYBE EVEN GEORGE THE DOORMAN...

EXCUSE ME, SIR. COULD I SEE YOUR PASS PLEASE?

MEGABANK

Alex PEATTIE + TAYLOR

I'M AFRAID I SHALL HAVE TO RESCIND MY PERMISSION TO USE NIGEL AS A SUBJECT FOR YOUR DOCUMENTARY IN THE CITY...

BUT WHY?

BECAUSE IT'S A BROKER'S JOB TO TALK TO HIS CLIENTS AND BRING IN BUSINESS... AND NIGEL'S PERFORMANCE HAS SUFFERED NOTICABLY SINCE YOU'VE BEEN FILMING HIM...

BUT WE'RE USING UNOBTRUSIVE FLY-ON-THE-WALL TECHNIQUES..

WE'RE JUST MAKING A DISCREET FILMED DIARY OF HIS DAY-TO-DAY LIFE: ON THE TRAIN, IN THE OFFICE, IN THE WINE BAR...

I TELL YOU, IT'S IMPOSSIBLE FOR A BROKER TO DO HIS JOB UNDER THOSE CONDITIONS.

NONE OF HIS CONTACTS HAVE GIVEN HIM ANY INSIDER TIPS SINCE HE'S BEEN WIRED FOR SOUND...

Alex PEATTIE + TAYLOR

HAVE YOU HEARD- SOME ANARCHIST GROUP IS ORGANISING A "STOP THE CITY" DEMONSTRATION ON JUNE 18TH...

WHAT?! YOU'RE JOKING...

APPARENTLY THEY INTEND TO CAUSE MAXIMUM DISRUPTION TO THE WORKINGS OF THE CITY ON THAT DAY AND ARE TARGETTING CUSTARD PIE AMBUSHES ON A SERIES OF HIGH PROFILE FINANCIAL BIG-WIGS...

UNBELIEVABLE...

WHERE **DO** THEY GET THEIR IDEAS FROM? I MEAN, THE SHEER BLIND IGNORANCE OF THESE SOCIAL MISFITS AND TROUBLE-MAKERS BEGGARS BELIEF...

I KNOW...

JUNE 18TH?!! ANYBODY WHO IS ANYBODY WILL BE AT ROYAL ASCOT WON'T THEY? THE CITY WILL BE DESERTED...

EXACTLY. DON'T THOSE IDIOT TROTS HAVE DIARIES?

email: alex-cartoon@etgate.co.uk

47

Strip 1

Alex PEATTIE + TAYLOR

IT SEEMS THAT OUR BOSSES ARE TAKING THE MILLENNIUM BUG THREAT MORE SERIOUSLY THAN WE SUPPOSED...

NO-ONE HAS ANY REAL IDEA HOW RELIABLY OUR COMPUTER SYSTEMS, OR THOSE OF OTHER COMPANIES, WILL BE WORKING AFTER JANUARY 1ST, 2000 — IT'S ALL QUITE WORRYING...

SO IN ORDER TO AVERT ANY RISKS THERE'S GOING TO BE A GENERAL WINDING DOWN OF ALL THE BANK'S BUSINESS IN THE LAST QUARTER OF THIS YEAR...

BUT THAT'S THE ONLY TIME WE EVER _DO_ ANY WORK...

EXACTLY, RIGHT BEFORE BONUS TIME WHEN IT'S GOING TO MAKE THE MAXIMUM IMPRESSION ON THE BOSS... BLAST.

email: alex-cartoon@etgate.co.uk

Strip 2

Alex PEATTIE + TAYLOR

PERSONALLY I THINK THERE'S A LOAD OF ROT BEING TALKED ABOUT THE MILLENNIUM BUG AND GLOBAL MELTDOWN—

PEOPLE PREDICTING IT WILL LEAD TO A BREAKDOWN IN CIVILISATION. WELL, I'VE BEEN TALKING TO PEOPLE WHO KNOW – THE I.T. ENGINEERS RESPONSIBLE FOR OUR MILLENNIUM COMPLIANCE...

THEY'RE THE PEOPLE WHO WILL BE MANNING OUR COMPUTERS ON NEW YEAR'S DAY. THEY TOLD ME THEY DO CHECKS EVERY DAY AND THAT ALL THE NECESSARY Y2K PROVISIONS ARE IN PLACE...

...TINS OF SPAM... BAKED BEANS ...PILCHARDS.

Y2K COMPLIANCE

CHECK... HAVE YOU GOT THE GENERATOR AND THE SHOTGUN TO WARD OFF THE FOOD MOBS?

email: alex-cartoon@etgate.co.uk

Strip 3

Alex PEATTIE + TAYLOR

BAD NEWS, ALEX. ROGER BROOKS HAS JUST CALLED. HE'S DROPPED OUT OF GOING TO WIMBLEDON WITH YOU TOMORROW...

THAT'S OKAY. I DIDN'T WANT TO GO ANYWAY...

AN INVITATION TO THE FIRST WEEK AT WIMBLEDON TO WATCH A LOAD OF UNSEEDED NON-ENTITIES PLAYING IS NAFF AND AMOUNTS TO AN INSULT TO THE INVITEE...

AND ROGER BROOKS IS MY SECOND WORST CLIENT...

MR HARDCASTLE?

IF IT'S SUCH AN INSULT HOW COME YOU DIDN'T INVITE YOUR WORST CLIENT?

GET HIM ON THE PHONE AND SEE IF HE WANTS TO GO TO WIMBLEDON TOMORROW... FIRST WEEK PLUS THE SHORT NOTICE INDICATING HE WASN'T MY FIRST CHOICE... EVEN _HE_ SHOULD COTTON ON....

email: alex-cartoon@etgate.co.uk

Strip 4

Alex PEATTIE + TAYLOR

THE BANK'S COMPUTER SYSTEM IS STILL DOWN. IT COULD TAKE DAYS TO FIX. BLASTED INTERNET PORNOGRAPHY'S AT THE ROOT OF THIS...

THERE WAS ALWAYS A DANGER THAT A VIRUS COULD BE INADVERTENTLY DOWNLOADED, THAT'S WHY I ISSUED A DIRECTIVE MAKING THE POSSESSION OF INDECENT MATERIAL ON AN EMPLOYEE'S HARD DISK A SACKABLE OFFENCE.

OUR COMPUTER SYSTEM IS A VITAL RESOURCE. AMONG OTHER THINGS IT ALLOWS ME, INSTEAD OF HAVING TO CIRCULATE A TYPED MEMO, TO E-MAIL A DIRECTIVE LIKE THIS GLOBALLY AND INSTANTANEOUSLY TO ALL PERSONNEL.

YES.

...CAUSING 11,000 EMPLOYEES WORLDWIDE TO SIMULTANEOUSLY DELETE 100s OF MEGABYTES OF SMUTTY PICTURES FROM THEIR P.C.s...

WHICH OVERLOADED THE SYSTEM AND CRASHED IT... AHEM... YES.

email: alex-cartoon@etgate.co.uk

I SEE THERE HAVE BEEN SOME HITCHES IN THIS TAKEOVER OF YOUR BANK BY THAT GERMAN BANK, ALEX...

MM...?

THERE ARE DOUBTS ABOUT ÜBERBANK'S RELATIONSHIP WITH THE THIRD REICH, THAT IT MIGHT HAVE BEEN USED AS A FRONT FOR STORING WEALTH AND TREASURES LOOTED FROM OCCUPIED COUNTRIES...

WHO KNOWS? BACK IN THE DARK DAYS OF WORLD WAR TWO I EXPECT VAULTS WERE USED TO CONCEAL ALL MANNER OF THINGS...

ZZZ...

PSST... KEEP DIGGING, CLIVE...

CLIVE, OLD CHAP. THE TUNNEL'S JUST ABOUT FINISHED AND OUR ESCAPE IS SCHEDULED FOR THURSDAY.

GOOD SHOW.

OBVIOUSLY WE MUST DO EVERYTHING POSSIBLE TO AVOID DETECTION ONCE WE ARE OUT OF THE CAMP...

LOOK WHAT I'VE MANAGED TO RIG UP USING JUST A SPARE R.A.F. JACKET...

ER... BUT IT STILL LOOKS LIKE A SPARE R.A.F. JACKET...

EXACTLY. I'LL HANG IT ON THE BACK OF MY CHAIR TO MAKE IT LOOK LIKE I'M STILL HERE...

RIGHT, MEN. THE ESCAPE IS FIXED FOR TOMORROW NIGHT... WE'VE HAD OUR TOP ENGINEERS, FORGERS AND TAILORS WORKING ROUND THE CLOCK...

WE'VE DUG A TUNNEL, WE'VE GOT EXPERTLY MADE CLOTHES, FAKE I.D. CARDS AND TRAVEL PERMITS AND CURRENCY... HOLD ON, THAT'S CLIVE'S JOB. WHERE IS HE?

AS OUR ESCAPE ROUTE TAKES US THROUGH OCCUPIED HOLLAND I SENT HIM A NOTE SAYING WE'D NEED HIM TO RUN US UP SOME GILDERS...

GILDERS, CLIVE.

OH DAMNATION.

OH NO... WE'VE MISCALCULATED. OUR TUNNEL IS TWENTY YARDS SHORT OF THE WOODS...

BLAST. I'D BETTER TELL THE CHAPS.

WE'RE SHORT...

WE'RE SHORT...

WE'RE SHORT...

WE'RE SHORT.

WHAT?

THEY'RE ALL SHORT AND I'M LONG...

WELL, MY SPREAD ON PRISONERS ESCAPING IS CURRENTLY 78-82...

LET'S HOPE THERE'S NO PROBLEMS WITH THE TUNNEL...

Alex PEATTIE + TAYLOR

AFTER ALL THAT PRISON CAMP FOOD THIS DESSERT IS EXCELLENT...

KEEP YOUR VOICE DOWN, CLIVE...

WE MAY BE IN PARIS BUT THIS PLACE IS FULL OF GERMAN OFFICERS AND WE DON'T WANT TO GIVE OURSELVES AWAY...

I JUST WANT TO COMPLIMENT THE CHEF. DON'T WORRY MY FRENCH IS EXCELLENT...

MERCI, GARÇON. C'ÉTAIT VRAIMENT "LA PIECE DE RESISTANCE"

RESISTANCE?

CRÉTIN...

email: alex-cartoon@etgate.co.uk

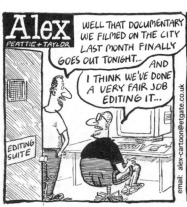
Alex PEATTIE + TAYLOR

WELL THAT DOCUMENTARY WE FILMED ON THE CITY LAST MONTH FINALLY GOES OUT TONIGHT...

AND I THINK WE'VE DONE A VERY FAIR JOB EDITING IT...

EDITING SUITE

ONE OF OUR SUBJECTS, THAT STOCK-BROKER NIGEL, WAS WORRIED WE WERE GOING TO STITCH HIM UP, BUT WE'VE LEFT OUT ANYTHING HE MIGHT BE SUBSEQUENTLY EMBARRASSED BY.

WE'VE LOST HIS CAROUSING IN THE LAP DANCING BAR, HIS COLLAPSING IN A DRUNKEN STUPOR, HIS FALLING ASLEEP ON THE TRAIN... AND JUST KEPT IN THE BITS WITH HIM WORKING AT HIS DESK

HE SHOULD BE PLEASED.

WE LIKE THE LOOK OF BROMEX. DEFINITELY A BUY...

THE B*ST*RDS! THEY'VE STITCHED ME UP! BROMEX'S PRICE HAS NOSE-DIVED SINCE THEN...

****! I HOPE NONE OF MY CLIENTS ARE WATCHING...

email: alex-cartoon@etgate.co.uk

Alex PEATTIE + TAYLOR

YOU'VE BEEN FINANCE DIRECTOR AT BROMEX FOR YEARS NOW, COLIN. ANY THOUGHTS OF RETIREMENT?

WELL, I'M SIXTY NEXT YEAR SO THE OPTION'S THERE. AS YOU CAN IMAGINE MY WIFE'S BRINGING A LOT OF PRESSURE TO BEAR ON ME ON THAT ISSUE...

SHE HAS THIS VISION OF US IN THE FULLNESS OF OUR YEARS SPENDING QUALITY TIME TOGETHER INDULGING IN ALL OUR SHARED INTERESTS AND LEISURE PURSUITS...

NO MORE FREE INVITES TO WIMBLEDON, ASCOT, THE CHELSEA FLOWER SHOW, GLYNDEBOURNE...? YOU TAKE THAT PENSION OVER MY DEAD BODY...

AS YOU SAY, DARLING.

MEGABANK HOSPITALITY TENT

WIMBLEDON '96

email: alex-cartoon@etgate.co.uk

Alex PEATTIE + TAYLOR

ARE YOU A JOURNALIST TOO?

YES, AND I THINK EVERYONE ON THIS PLANE IS. I'M GREG MASTERLEY, DAILY BUGLE.

AFTER ALL NICK LEESON IS UP FRONT IN FIRST CLASS BEING FLOWN BACK TO BRITAIN FROM SINGAPORE. EVERYONE'S DESPERATE TO GET AN INTERVIEW, THOUGH RUMOUR HAS IT HE'S ALREADY SOLD HIS EXCLUSIVE STORY TO A PAPER FOR A LARGE SUM.

THIS SITUATION RAISES A SERIOUS QUESTION OF PRESS ETHICS. NAMELY SHOULD AN INDIVIDUAL BE ALLOWED TO PERSONALLY PROFIT FROM HAVING COMMITTED FRAUD

I'M AFRAID IT'S JUST STANDARD JOURNALISTIC PRACTICE.

US CLAIMING FOR FIRST CLASS ON OUR EXPENSES BUT TRAVELLING ECONOMY?

EXACTLY. WE'LL WAIT TILL LEESON GOES TO THE LOO AND THEN NAB HIM.

FIRST CLASS AND TOILET

Alex PEATTIE + TAYLOR

PENNY, I THINK I SHOULD WARN YOU. OCTOBER'S GOING TO BE VERY HECTIC WORKWISE. YOU MIGHT NOT SEE MUCH OF ME...

OH...WHAT'S GOING ON?

THE STOCK MARKET GOES OVER TO CONTINENTAL TIME NEXT WEEK. MORNING MEETINGS WILL BE MOVED FORWARDS AN HOUR. THERE'S NOT EVEN A TRAIN I CAN CATCH THAT EARLY. I MAY NEED TO STAY OVER IN TOWN.

I SEE...

THEN THERE'S THE Y2K BUG. BANKS DON'T WANT TO RISK THEIR DEALING SYSTEMS IN THE RUN-UP TO 2000. SO WE'RE GOING TO HAVE TO DO A WHOLE QUARTER'S WORK IN ONE MONTH.

OCTOBER AGAIN?

'FRAID SO.

YOU GOT A PINK TICKET FOR THE WHOLE OF THE RUGBY WORLD CUP WITHOUT EVEN SACRIFICING ANY BROWNIE POINTS?!

PIECE OF CAKE.

WE ARE NOT WORTHY...

RUGBY WORLD CUP OCT '99

Alex PEATTIE + TAYLOR

SO WHAT ARE YOU DOING FOR THE MILLENNIUM, ALEX? GOING AWAY? GOT A BIG PARTY PLANNED?

ACTUALLY NOT, ROGER.

email: alex-cartoon@etgate.co.uk

THE CITY'S TAKING THE THREAT POSED TO ITS COMPUTER SYSTEMS BY THE Y2K BUG VERY SERIOUSLY. BANKS ARE FEARFUL OF LEAVING ANY OPEN POSITIONS OR DEALS ON JANUARY 1ST...

MANY ARE GOING SO FAR AS TO CLOSE DOWN THEIR OPERATIONS FROM MID-NOVEMBER TO BE BETTER PREPARED FOR THE CRISIS...ALL IN ALL I CAN HARDLY MAKE SOCIAL PLANS FOR NEW YEAR.

YOU'RE ANTICIPATING HAVING TO BE ON HAND TO MONITOR THE PROBLEM?

ER, NO. I'M ANTICIPATING BEING SENSATIONALLY HUNG-OVER FROM SIX WEEKS OF UNINTERRUPTED CHRISTMAS PARTYING...

Alex PEATTIE + TAYLOR

I'M TRYING TO CALL MARTIN JAMES AT MINERAL BANK BUT HE DOESN'T SEEM TO BE ANSWERING HIS EXTENSION...

BRR... BRR....

email: alex-cartoon@etgate.co.uk

MARTIN JAMES? DIDN'T YOU HEAR? HE GOT MADE REDUNDANT YESTERDAY...

WHAT? YOU'RE KIDDING. WHY DIDN'T ANYONE TELL ME? HE'S AN OLD FRIEND OF MINE.

WHERE'S HIS HOME NUMBER? AH YES... HERE WE ARE: 0-1-7-1-4-6-8-...

YOU'RE GIVING HIM A RING TO COMMISERATE?

PLICK PLICK

NO. I'M PROGRAMMING IT INTO THE MEMORY SO WHEN HE PHONES BEGGING FOR A JOB HERE THE CALLER I.D. DISPLAY WILL SHOW ME NOT TO BOTHER PICKING IT UP...

PLICK PLICK

Alex PEATTIE + TAYLOR

OF COURSE IN ADDITION TO THE MILLENNIUM BUG THERE'S ALSO THE DANGER OF Y2K FRAUD...

email: alex-cartoon@etgate.co.uk

ALL THE UNCERTAINTY COULD PERMIT THE LAUNDERING OR EVEN MISAPPROPRIATION OF MONEY, WITH THE BLAME FOR ANY SUBSEQUENT FINANCIAL DISCREPANCIES BEING PUT ON THE BUG...

ONE WONDERS IF OUR NOTORIOUSLY COMPUTER-ILLITERATE BOSSES ARE AWARE OF THE WAY THE SITUATION IN JANUARY MAY BE EXPLOITED BY UNSCRUPULOUS INDIVIDUALS...

LET'S HOPE NOT, EH?

IT'D BE THE PERFECT EXCUSE TO AVOID PAYING OUR XMAS BONUSES BY CLAIMING THE WHOLE POOL HAD VANISHED...

61

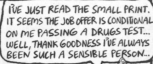

Strip 1

DARLING, THIS LETTER OF ACCEPTANCE I RECEIVED LAST WEEK FOR MY NEW JOB AT MEGABANK...

WHAT ABOUT IT, DARLING?

I'VE JUST READ THE SMALL PRINT. IT SEEMS THE JOB OFFER IS CONDITIONAL ON ME PASSING A DRUGS TEST... WELL, THANK GOODNESS I'VE ALWAYS BEEN SUCH A SENSIBLE PERSON...

SO MANY CITY TRADERS HAVE THIS RISKY, SELF DESTRUCTIVE, IMPULSE-LED WILD STREAK. THEY LIKE TO LIVE DANGEROUSLY. WHEREAS MY NATURAL PERSONALITY IS TO BE PRUDENT, CAUTIOUS AND LEVEL-HEADED...

THAT'S TRUE, DARLING

...SHAME ABOUT ALL THOSE DRUGS YOU TAKE THOUGH... YOU'LL NEVER PASS THE TEST...

YES, BUT AT LEAST I DIDN'T ALREADY IMPETUOUSLY GO IN AND RESIGN MY CURRENT JOB.

RIP RIP

Strip 2

YOU BROKERS ARE JUST GLORIFIED GOOD-TIME BOYS. DON'T YOU THINK YOUR DAYS IN THE CITY ARE NUMBERED?

I MEAN, YOUR CLIENTS, THE FUND MANAGERS ARE HARD-WORKING HIGHLY-MOTIVATED INDIVIDUALS WHO SPEND THEIR DAYS STUDYING GRAPHS, STATISTICS, COMPANY REPORTS AND ANALYST'S NOTES...

BUT SO MUCH OF THAT INFORMATION CAN NOW BE ACQUIRED BY THEM DIRECTLY OFF THE INTERNET OR FROM THEIR OWN IN-HOUSE RESEARCH. WHAT ADDED VALUE SERVICE DO YOU THINK YOU GIVE THEM?

THE ILLUSION OF HAVING A SOCIAL LIFE AND SOME FRIENDS?

WHO ELSE WOULD VOLUNTARILY TAKE THEM OUT FOR DRINKS?

Strip 3

SO YOU'RE HAVING STEVENS "REVERSE HEADHUNTED"...

WELL, HE'S NOT REALLY UP TO HIS JOB AND SACKING HIM WOULD COST US MONEY...

SO WITHOUT HIS KNOWLEDGE I'VE GOT A TAME HEADHUNTER TRYING TO FIND HIM ANOTHER JOB. IT SOUNDS SNEAKY BUT IT'S ACTUALLY QUITE PRINCIPLED BY CITY STANDARDS...

I'M SHOWING STEVENS RESPECT AND CONSIDERATION, I'M AVOIDING CAUSING HIM DISTRESS OR CREATING BAD BLOOD, PLUS I'M ALLOWING HIM TO RETAIN HIS PRIDE AND NOT FEEL REJECTED. OF COURSE ONE DOES EXPECT A CERTAIN TYPE OF BEHAVIOUR IN RETURN...

YES... THE OPPOSITE...

LITTLE FOOL... WHAT'S HE BOTHERING TO BE LOYAL FOR?

NO THANK YOU. I'M PERFECTLY HAPPY WHERE I AM...

Strip 4

THESE TAKEOVER DEALS YOU ORGANISE, ALEX. HOW DO YOU PUT THEM TOGETHER? JUST WITH AN EYE FOR A QUICK PROFIT FOR MANAGEMENT?

I MEAN THEY NEVER BENEFIT THE EMPLOYEES, DO THEY?

ACTUALLY, PENNY, MERGERS COME ABOUT THROUGH IDENTIFYING "SYNERGIES"; THAT IS AREAS OF CROSSOVER BETWEEN THEIR BUSINESSES...

"SYNERGY"? THAT'S JUST ABSTRACT CORPORATE GOBBLEDEGOOK.

FAR FROM IT, PENNY. IT'S ACTUALLY A PRECISE MEASURABLE SCIENTIFIC QUOTIENT...

SO HOW MANY "SYNERGIES" DO WE HAVE IN YOUR TAKEOVER PROPOSAL, ALEX?

ABOUT 20,000, SIR BRIAN. YOU CAN LOSE 10% THROUGH NATURAL WASTAGE AND SACK THE REST...

email: alex-cartoon@etgate.co.uk

Alex PEATTIE + TAYLOR

Panel 1: DARLING, DON'T FORGET IT'S THE NEIGHBOURHOOD FIREWORKS PARTY TONIGHT. — OH RIGHT.

Panel 2: YOU KNOW WHAT A DAD'S PRESENCE AT A BIG COMMUNITY SOCIAL OCCASION LIKE THIS MEANS TO HIS KIDS, SO PLEASE MAKE A BIT OF AN EFFORT THIS YEAR. — I WILL...

Panel 3: YOUR SON'S SO PROUD OF YOU AND YOU LET HIM DOWN BADLY IN FRONT OF ALL HIS FRIENDS LAST YEAR. — IT WON'T HAPPEN AGAIN I PROMISE.

Panel 4: THANK GOODNESS DAD DIDN'T COME... HE LOOKED LIKE A RIGHT LOSER LAST YEAR TURNING UP AND SHOWING EVERYONE ELSE HE HAD NO WORK ON... — WOOOSH BANG — YES, DEAR.

email: alex-cartoon@etgate.co.uk

Alex PEATTIE + TAYLOR

Panel 1: TODAY'S A SPECIAL DAY. DO YOU KNOW WHY, CHARLIE? — YES, OF COURSE, UNCLE CLIVE. — WOOSH — OOH...

Panel 2: MY MUMMY SAYS IT'S A RITUAL OCCASION. IT'S ABOUT A VERY NAUGHTY MAN WHO DID A BAD THING AND HAD TO BE PUNISHED... — THAT'S RIGHT.

Panel 3: SHE TOLD ME THERE WERE GOING TO BE FIREWORKS, BUT THIS IS AMAZING... LOOK...

Panel 4: DADDY ARRIVED DRUNK FROM THE RUGBY WORLD CUP FINAL AND THREW UP IN THE BONFIRE...

email: alex-cartoon@etgate.co.uk

Alex PEATTIE + TAYLOR

Panel 1: NOT LIKE YOU TO COMPLIMENT ONE OF OUR RIVAL BROKERS, TIM. — PRAISE WHERE PRAISE IS DUE, NICK.

Panel 2: I FULLY COMMEND MEGABANK'S DECISION TO HOLD A "CHARITY DAY" TOMORROW WHERE THE BROKERS DONATE THEIR ENTIRE DAY'S EARNINGS TO WORTHY CAUSES...

Panel 3: IT'S A GESTURE THAT'S BEING WIDELY SUPPORTED IN THE CITY. I JUST THINK IT'S WONDERFUL SEEING A COMPANY REALLY DOING SOMETHING TO HELP OTHERS... — UNDERPRIVILEGED KIDS?

Panel 4: NO. YOU AND ME. NO POINT IN US COMING INTO WORK TOMORROW AS ALL THE CLIENTS WILL BE GIVING THEIR BUSINESS TO MEGABANK. — THAT'S TRUE... FANCY PLAYING SOME GOLF?

email: alex-cartoon@etgate.co.uk

Alex PEATTIE + TAYLOR

Panel 1: OUR BOY'S GETTING REALLY EXCITED ABOUT CHRISTMAS ALREADY. HE KNOWS EXACTLY WHAT TOYS HE WANTS...

Panel 2: HE'S SEVEN NOW SO I'VE ASKED MY HUSBAND TO SIT DOWN AND HAVE A TALK WITH HIM, ABOUT CHRISTMAS AND ALL THAT...

Panel 3: YOU KNOW, HOW IT REALLY WORKS, WHERE THE PRESENTS ACTUALLY COME FROM ETC. IT SEEMS SILLY TO ALLOW HIM TO REMAIN IN IGNORANCE ANY LONGER AT HIS AGE....

Panel 4: SO THERE'S THIS WEBSITE WHERE YOU BUY THE TOYS ON-LINE AND HAVE THEM DELIVERED TO YOUR HOUSE. GIVE ME YOUR CREDIT CARD NUMBER AND I CAN SORT OUT ALL MY OWN PRESENTS... — OH... I SEE... YES...

email: alex-cartoon@etgate.co.uk

Alex — PEATTIE + TAYLOR

WITH SO MUCH BUSINESS CORRESPONDENCE BEING DONE ELECTRONICALLY THESE DAYS AUTHENTICITY CAN BE A PROBLEM...

SOME BUSINESSMEN HAVE A DIGITALLY-SCANNED FACSIMILE OF THEIR SIGNATURE ON THEIR COMPUTER WHICH CAN BE AUTOMATICALLY ATTACHED TO ANY LETTER

email: alex-cartoon@etgate.co.uk

NOT ME THOUGH. FOR ME IT DOESN'T CARRY THE WEIGHT AND AUTHORITY OF A PRINTED HARD COPY WITH A GENUINE INK SIGNATURE...

YOUR SECRETARY'S PP-ING ON BEHALF OF YOU?

EXACTLY. HOW ELSE CAN I IMPRESS ON MY CORRESPONDENT HOW BUSY I AM?

PRINT

Alex — PEATTIE + TAYLOR

MIGHT I REMIND YOU THAT UNDER THE TERMS OF YOUR "GARDENING LEAVE" YOU ARE CONTRACTUALLY PROHIBITED FROM ALL CONTACT WITH CLIENTS...

e-mail: alex-cartoon@etgate.co.uk

THE REASON YOU ARE BEING PAID TO STAY AT HOME FOR 3 MONTHS IS TO KEEP YOU OUT OF THE MARKET BEFORE YOU START WORK FOR A NEW ORGANISATION...

ANY CONTACT, BUSINESS OR SOCIAL, YOU HAVE WITH ANY CLIENT OVER THIS PERIOD COULD BE INTERPRETED AS "ENTICEMENT" AND COULD BE USED AS THE BASIS FOR LEGAL ACTION BY YOUR FORMER EMPLOYER...

RIGHT... ER... YES...

...YOU'RE VERY WELL UP ON ALL THIS, DARLING.

THIS IS THE ONE XMAS WHERE YOU WON'T GET AWAY WITH GOING OUT ON THE LASH CLAIMING IT'S "IMPORTANT CLIENT ENTERTAINMENT"...

SO KEEP BABY SITTING TILL I GET BACK.

Alex — PEATTIE + TAYLOR

ANOTHER EVENING WORKING LATE. ANOTHER EVENING WHEN YOU'LL MISS LITTLE CHRISTOPHER'S BED TIME. HOPEFULLY OUR NANNY WILL STILL BE UP, CLIVE.

HOW WOULD A MODERN STRESSED-OUT EXECUTIVE MANAGE WORKING IN THE COMPETITIVE HIGH-PRESSURE WORLD OF THE CITY WITHOUT HIS FULL-TIME LIVE-IN NANNY?

SHE'LL HAVE TAKEN CHRISTOPHER DOWN TO THE PARK, MAYBE TO A KIDDIES' PARTY WITH HIS FRIENDS... I'LL LOOK FORWARD TO GETTING A FULL RUN-DOWN OF THE DAY'S HIGHLIGHTS WHEN I GET BACK...

THE LOVETTS' NANNY SAYS THEY'VE CANCELLED THEIR CHATEAU IN THE LOIRE NEXT SUMMER. NO BONUS THERE OBVIOUSLY... OLIVER'S DAD IS AT HOME A LOT... LOOKS LIKE HE'S BEEN SACKED...

EXCELLENT.

DADDY!

DO SHUT UP, CHRISTOPHER.

Alex — PEATTIE + TAYLOR

ONE OF MY RESPONSIBILITIES AS HEAD OF HUMAN RESOURCES IS STAFF TRAINING AND I THINK I SHOULD START WITH MY OWN DEPARTMENT...

YOU, FOR EXAMPLE, PETER, YOU COULD BENEFIT FROM A BODY LANGUAGE COURSE. LEARN THE BUSINESS ADVANTAGES OF A POSITIVE POSTURE, A STRONG HANDSHAKE, MAKING FIRM EYE CONTACT...

I JUST SAW THE WAY YOU GREETED CLIVE WHEN YOU JUST PASSED HIM. LIMP HANDSHAKE, NO EYE CONTACT, CLOSED AND DEFENSIVE BODY LANGUAGE... WHAT DO YOU THINK THAT SAYS TO HIM?

email: alex-cartoon@etgate.co.uk

THE TRUTH. THAT HE'S GOT A TINY BONUS COMING TO HIM...

EXACTLY, MAN. WE DON'T WANT THEM TO BE ABLE TO GUESS THAT INFORMATION BEFORE IT'S ANNOUNCED NEXT WEEK...

2000

71

Row 1

WHAT'S THIS, ROBIN?

IT'S A START-UP PROPOSAL FOR AN INTERNET COMPANY PUT TOGETHER BY A COUPLE OF FRIENDS OF MINE...

THEY'VE WORKED OUT A DETAILED BUSINESS PLAN AND ESTIMATE THEY'LL NEED TO RAISE £5 MILLION.

MOST THOROUGH I'M SURE, BUT THIS'LL HAVE TO BE REWRITTEN AND REFORMATTED...

YOU AND YOUR TRENDY FRIENDS MAY KNOW ALL ABOUT E-COMMERCE, BUT I KNOW HOW TO PRESENT A PITCH THAT WILL PERSUADE TODAY'S VENTURE CAPITALISTS TO GET ON BOARD...

JOT IT DOWN ON THE BACK OF A BEERMAT AND WE'LL TELL EVERYONE IT WAS THOUGHT UP IN A FLASH LAST WEEK...

YOU GREEDY B*ST*RDS ARE SUCH ROMANTICS.

email: alex-cartoon@etgate.co.uk

Row 2

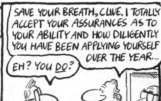

LOOK, RUPERT, I JUST WANT TO MENTION HOW HARD I'VE WORKED OVER THE LAST YEAR...

AH... BONUS TIME GROVELLING.

SAVE YOUR BREATH, CLIVE. I TOTALLY ACCEPT YOUR ASSURANCES AS TO YOUR ABILITY AND HOW DILIGENTLY YOU HAVE BEEN APPLYING YOURSELF OVER THE YEAR...

EH? YOU DO?

NATURALLY, CLIVE. I SHALL ASSUME YOU ARE AS BRILLIANT AS YOU CLAIM AND I THINK YOU WILL FIND THAT YOUR REQUIREMENTS WILL BE ADEQUATELY MET BY THE BONUS I SHALL BE AWARDING YOU...

A VERY SMALL ONE PRESUMABLY.

WELL IF HE'S AS GOOD AS HE SAYS HE'LL HAVE PUNTED ALL HIS SAVINGS ON INTERNET STOCK AND MADE HIMSELF A FORTUNE...

IT'S THE NEW CATCH 22...

email: alex-cartoon@etgate.co.uk

Row 3

I'M LOOKING FORWARD TO NEXT WEEK AT WORK. I CAN TELL YOU THE TENSION AT THE OFFICE WILL BE PALPABLE...

QUITE A FEW PEOPLE WILL HAVE HAD SLEEPLESS NIGHTS OVER THE WEEKEND KNOWING THAT THEY ARE SOON TO FIND OUT IN REAL TERMS WHETHER THEY ARE ANY GOOD AT THEIR JOBS.

WHAT ARE YOU ON ABOUT, ALEX?

BONUSES, PENNY, THE PAYING OUT OF OUR ANNUAL BONUSES...

BUT, ALEX, YOU ALL GOT THOSE YESTERDAY...

I'M TALKING ABOUT OUR BOSSES... ACCORDING TO HOW MANY PEOPLE RESIGN THEY'LL FIND OUT IF THEY GOT THEIR SUMS WRONG AND PAID THEMSELVES TOO MUCH OF THE MONEY...

email: alex-cartoon@etgate.co.uk

Row 4

SO WE'VE LOST ONE OF OUR TOP ANALYSTS?

YES. BANKED HIS BONUS CHEQUE AND DID A BUNK. NOTHING I OFFERED COULD PERSUADE HIM TO STAY.

WHAT SORT OF MONSTERS HAVE WE CREATED? I KNOW WE'RE IN PART TO BLAME. AFTER ALL WE'VE HAD TO PAY OUT SALARIES AT THE SAME LEVEL AS OUR COMPETITORS TO KEEP PEOPLE...

SHUDDER

BUT WHEN I SEE THE COMPLACENCY AND SELF-INTEREST THAT SOME OF OUR EMPLOYEES SHOW... THEY'LL KICK US IN THE TEETH AND TURN THEIR BACKS ON THE PRINCIPLES WE'VE TRIED TO INSTIL IN THEM...

TOTAL GREED AND MATERIALISM? YES, IT'S ANNOYING WHEN SOMEONE GOES OFF TO BUM ROUND THE WORLD FOR 18 MONTHS.

SADLY HE'S NOW SO RICH HE DOESN'T GIVE A DAMN ANY MORE.

email: alex-cartoon@etgate.co.uk

74

Alex — PEATTIE + TAYLOR

Panel 1: SO YOU GOT SACKED FROM YOUR JOB AS THE DAILY BUGLE'S SHARE TIPSTER, DAN? WHAT HAPPENED..?

Panel 2: WELL, IN THE WAKE OF ALL THESE ACCUSATIONS ABOUT FINANCIAL JOURNALISTS BUYING SHARES IN ADVANCE OF WRITING FAVORABLY ABOUT THEM, MY EDITOR INVESTIGATED ME...

Panel 3: HE FOUND I HAD INDEED BEEN PURCHASING STOCKS IN ADVANCE OF TIPPING THEM IN MY COLUMN. HE SAID HE HAD NO OPTION BUT TO DISMISS ME, ESPECIALLY WHEN IT BECAME CLEAR THE AMOUNT OF MONEY I'D BEEN MAKING...
HOW MUCH?

Panel 4: ER... NONE AT ALL. THE SHARE PRICES NEVER MOVED...
OH DEAR... DAMNING EVIDENCE THAT NO-ONE IN THE MARKETS TAKES THE BLINDEST BIT OF NOTICE OF WHAT YOU WRITE...

email: alex-cartoon@etgate.co.uk

Alex — PEATTIE + TAYLOR

Panel 1: I'M GETTING A LOT OF STICK FROM MY FELLOW ANALYSTS JUST BECAUSE I HAPPEN TO COVER TECHNOLOGY STOCKS...

Panel 2: ALL THE INVESTORS WANT TO TALK TO ME ABOUT THE FORTUNES TO BE MADE FROM INTERNET COMPANIES, AND NO ONE GIVES A DAMN ABOUT UTILITIES, ENGINEERING OR PETROCHEMICALS ANY MORE...

Panel 3: BUT MY JOB'S NO DODDLE. PRODUCING RESEARCH ON THIS RADICAL, COMPLEX, TOTALLY UNPRECEDENTED AND CONSTANTLY DEVELOPING SECTOR BRINGS ITS OWN PRESSURES I CAN ASSURE YOU...

Panel 4: YOU TRY PADDING OUT "BUY THEM BECAUSE THEY'RE GOING UP" INTO 5000 WORDS...
SO YOU DON'T UNDERSTAND IT EITHER, EH?

email: alex-cartoon@etgate.co.uk

Alex — PEATTIE + TAYLOR

Panel 1: COME ON, ALEX TELL US ABOUT THAT ASTON MARTIN YOU'RE GOING TO BUY WITH YOUR BONUS.
WHAT'S THE POINT?

Panel 2: BUT YOU ALWAYS LOOK FORWARD TO THIS TIME OF YEAR WHEN WE ALL BANK STONKING BIG BONUS CHEQUES AND THE GRADUATE GETS FOBBED OFF WITH A TOKEN PITTANCE...

Panel 3: ...WE'RE ALL BOASTING ABOUT THE CARS WE'RE GOING TO BUY WHILE THE TRAINEE IS WAILING ABOUT HOW HE'S STRUGGLING TO MEET THE BILLS...WELL, IT'S HAPPENED...
YES...
I DON'T KNOW HOW I'M GOING TO COPE FINANCIALLY...

Panel 4: ...WITH THE FISCAL YEAR END COMING UP I'M GOING TO GET CLOBBERED ON CAPITAL GAINS TAX THANKS TO ALL THE MONEY I'VE MADE ON INVESTING IN MY FRIENDS' INTERNET START-UPS...

email: alex-cartoon@etgate.co.uk

Alex — PEATTIE + TAYLOR

Panel 1: YOU KNOW, CLIVE, THE INTERNET IS REALLY CHANGING THE WAY PEOPLE THINK.
THAT'S VERY TRUE, ALEX.

Panel 2: WHEN YOU HEAR A CONVERSATION BETWEEN BUSINESS TRAVELLERS THESE DAYS THEY SEEM TO BE SPEAKING A FOREIGN LANGUAGE.
ONE FEELS TOTALLY OUT OF TOUCH...

Panel 3: E-COMMERCE HAS ENGENDERED A WHOLE NEW ATTITUDE AND PRINCIPLES THAT ARE TOTALLY AT ODDS WITH THE WAY WE ONCE LIVED AND WORKED...
YES...

Panel 4: SIGH: WHATEVER HAPPENED TO CONSPICUOUS CONSUMPTION?
PEOPLE THESE DAYS BOAST ABOUT SAVING MONEY...
MY TICKET ONLY COST £132 FROM PLANEBOOKER-COM...
WELL I GOT MINE FOR £108 AT LOTSAFLIGHTS-COM...

email: alex-cartoon@etgate.co.uk

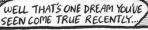

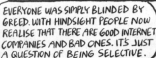

Alex PEATTIE + TAYLOR

FRANKLY, MARTHA, I THINK IT'S UNFAIR THAT YOU SEEM TO BE GETTING THE BLAME FOR THE DEMISE OF THE DOT.COM MARKET.

EVERYONE WAS SIMPLY BLINDED BY GREED. WITH HINDSIGHT PEOPLE NOW REALISE THAT THERE ARE GOOD INTERNET COMPANIES AND BAD ONES. IT'S JUST A QUESTION OF BEING SELECTIVE.

AS AN INVESTMENT BANKER HANDLING A FLOAT TODAY, ALL I'D ASK MYSELF IS :- WOULD I USE THIS SERVICE MYSELF? AND IN THE CASE OF LASTMINUTE-COM THE ANSWER HAS STILL GOT TO BE "YES"...

THANKYOU.

...AFTER ALL ONE WOULD WANT TO BE ABLE TO BOOK ONESELF OFF ON A FOREIGN HOLIDAY AT SHORT NOTICE TO AVOID ALL THE FLAK WHEN THE DEAL GOES BELLY-UP...

"TAP TAP"

email: alex-cartoon@etgate.co.uk

Alex PEATTIE + TAYLOR

FORGET IT, RUPERT... I KNOW YOU'VE BEEN SENT BY THE BOARD TO TRY TO TALK ME INTO TAKING EARLY RETIREMENT BUT IT WON'T WORK...

HEAR ME OUT, DAVID...

I JUST WANT TO PAINT A PICTURE FOR YOU. YOU'RE FIFTY-EIGHT NOW. JUST IMAGINE IT: A LIFE WHERE THERE ARE NO DEMANDS ON YOU, NO ONE TELLING YOU WHAT TO DO OR HOW TO BE...

YOU GET UP IN THE MORNING AND SLIP INTO AN OLD COMFORTABLE PAIR OF SHOES, YOUR FAVOURITE TWEED JACKET, A WELL-LOVED SWEATER, MAYBE A RATHER ANCIENT AND BATTERED HAT...

HOLD ON...

YOU MEAN THE BANK'S _SERIOUS_ ABOUT BRINGING IN PERMANENT DRESS DOWN?

EXACTLY. SO FOR GOD'S SAKE JUST RETIRE WITH DIGNITY. YOU KNOW YOU'VE GOT NO DRESS SENSE AND YOU'LL BE A LAUGHING STOCK...

email: alex-cartoon@etgate.co.uk

Alex PEATTIE + TAYLOR

YOU KNOW, ROBIN, I REMEMBER WHEN HAVING A MOBILE PHONE WAS A STATUS SYMBOL. SIMPLY SPEAKING INTO ONE ON A TRAIN IMPLIED YOU WERE HAVING AN IMPORTANT BUSINESS CONVERSATION...

MUST HAVE BEEN A MILLION YEARS B.C., ALEX. NOWADAYS YOU'RE JUST AS LIKELY TO BE A BUILDER, A HOUSEWIFE OR A SCHOOLKID PHONING UP A FRIEND FOR A CHAT...

YES. SADLY THEY'RE TEN A-PENNY THESE DAYS.

OF COURSE THERE'S STILL PRESTIGE TO BE GAINED FROM HAVING A MODEL WITH THE LATEST GIMMICKS...VOICE-ACTIVATED DIALLING FOR EXAMPLE...

"ROBIN THORNE...WORK."

YOU REALLY THINK SO?

"BLIP BRR BRR"

RING RING.

=AHEM= "SIR JEREMY CHOLMONDLEY...HOME."

email: alex-cartoon@etgate.co.uk

Alex PEATTIE + TAYLOR

IT'S MOST ANNOYING. NONE OF THE CLIENTS WANT TO TALK TO ME ABOUT THE INTERNET ANY MORE...

THAT DOT.COM STUFF'S RATHER OUT OF FASHION AT THE MOMENT, ROBIN...

AND NOW WE'VE GOT TO SEE MR HARDCASTLE ABOUT A DEAL IN THE ENGINEERING SECTOR. THAT'S _OLD_ ECONOMY...

ONCE UPON A TIME NOT EVERYTHING WAS DIGITAL AND ON-LINE. THERE ARE SERIOUS GAPS IN YOUR EXPERIENCE AS AN INVESTMENT BANKER...

email: alex-cartoon@etgate.co.uk

LOOK ON THIS AS A CHANCE TO GAIN AN INSIGHT INTO TRADITIONAL MANUFACTURING PROCESSES WHERE A PRODUCT IS PHYSICALLY MADE BY MACHINERY WITH COGS LEVERS AND MOVING PARTS...

OH WELL... WHY NOT?

I SEE YOU'VE GOT YOUNG ROBIN PHOTOCOPYING AT LAST...

FORTY COPIES OF HARDCASTLE'S DRAFT AGREEMENT BY ELEVEN.

Strip 1

 POSH SOCIETY IS A VERY HYPOCRITICAL PLACE. I AGREE... YOU JUST GET JUDGED BY YOUR APPEARANCE...

 I MEAN A LOT OF CITY INSTITUTIONS HAVE RELAXED THEIR DRESS CODES RECENTLY WHICH MEANS YOU GET A LOT OF PEOPLE LIKE US COMING INTO WORK IN OUR CASUAL CLOTHES.

  WE'RE STILL THE SAME PEOPLE UNDERNEATH BUT JUST BECAUSE WE'RE NOT WEARING FORMAL BUSINESS DRESS ANY MORE WE GET TREATED TOTALLY DIFFERENTLY BY THOSE SNOOTY WAITERS... YEAH. RESTAURANT

  THEY ACTUALLY LET US INTO THEIR RESTAURANTS NOW DON'T THEY, STONKER? THAT'S RIGHT, GUTBUCKET... THEY USED TO BAN US ON SIGHT WHEN WE WERE STILL ON THE LIFFE FLOOR AND WEARING OUR STRIPEY BLAZERS...

email: alex-cartoon@etgate.co.uk

Strip 2

 FOLLOWING THE EXAMPLE OF OTHER AMERICAN BANKS WE SHALL BE INTRODUCING A PERMANENT DRESS DOWN POLICY.

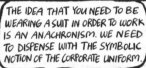  THE IDEA THAT YOU NEED TO BE WEARING A SUIT IN ORDER TO WORK IS AN ANACHRONISM. WE NEED TO DISPENSE WITH THE SYMBOLIC NOTION OF THE CORPORATE UNIFORM.

 EMPLOYEES SHOULD BE ENCOURAGED TO FEEL COMFORTABLE ABOUT DOING THEIR JOBS DRESSED IN CASUAL CLOTHES. AFTER ALL WE LIVE IN THE AGE OF THE INTERNET, THE PALM PILOT, THE WAP MOBILE PHONE.

 SO WE CAN MAKE OUR PEOPLE WORK RIGHT ROUND THE CLOCK. AND THIS WAY WE CAN ERADICATE THE FEELING THAT ONCE YOU THROW YOUR SUIT OFF IN THE EVENING YOUR TIME IS YOUR OWN...

email: alex-cartoon@etgate.co.uk

Strip 3

 BAD NEWS ABOUT THAT FLOTATION WE'VE BEEN WORKING ON FOR THE INTERNET COMPANY THAT OFFERS ON-LINE NUTRITIONAL ADVICE FOR PET OWNERS... DOGSBREAKFAST.COM?

 YES. IT'S BEEN PULLED DUE TO ADVERSE STOCKMARKET CONDITIONS... WHICH MEANS NO FEES FOR US... BLAST... THAT'S THE FIFTH THIS MONTH...

 THAT'S RIGHT. I IMAGINE THE BANK MUST BE STARTING TO FEEL THE FINANCIAL CONSEQUENCES OF THE GENERAL DEMISE OF THE NEW ECONOMY...

 I ESTIMATE WE SHOULD SAVE A FORTUNE ON THE DEPARTMENTAL WAGE BILL... YES. PEOPLE CAN NO LONGER FLOUNCE IN HERE DEMANDING A BIG PAY RISE TO STOP THEM DEFECTING TO A DOT-COM...

email: alex-cartoon@etgate.co.uk

Strip 4

 OH WELL, IT LOOKS LIKE THE LUCRATIVE MARKET FOR INTERNET COMPANIES IS OVER FOR THE FORSEEABLE FUTURE...

 SO IT'S BACK TO PUTTING TOGETHER MERGERS OF GOOD OLD-FASHIONED MANUFACTURING BUSINESSES FOR ME. STILL, IT'S A RELIEF IN SOME WAYS...

 ARRANGING TAKEOVERS OF INTERNET COMPANIES PRESENTED PROBLEMS THAT TAXED THE MOST EXPERIENCED CORPORATE FINANCIERS... VALUING A BUSINESS THAT DOESN'T MAKE A PROFIT...?

 NO, TRYING TO THINK OF A CODE NAME FOR THE COMPANY THAT'S SILLIER THAN THE ACTUAL NAME...

email: alex-cartoon@etgate.co.uk

Alex
PEATTIE + TAYLOR

Strip 1:

VICTOR BLANK'S CHARITY CRICKET MATCH ALWAYS ATTRACTS THE TOP CITY BANKERS AS WELL AS MANY FORMER PLAYERS...

SEE THAT CHAP OVER THERE? THAT'S ALEX MASTERLEY OF MEGABANK. HE PLAYS EVERY YEAR. AS A BATSMAN HE'S CAPABLE OF CAUSING A FEW HEADACHES...

HE'S VERY TENACIOUS AND SINGLE-MINDED. ONCE HE GETS HIMSELF SETTLED HE'S A VERY HARD MAN FOR A TEAM TO GET OUT...

SO I SEE...

ALEX, YOU'RE BATTING. WILL YOU PLEASE GET OUT TO THE CREASE...

CAN'T YOU SEE I'M NETWORKING?

Strip 2:

IT'S JUST ANOTHER EXAMPLE OF THE LACK OF BASIC HUMAN CONSIDERATION SHOWN BY OUR MENFOLK'S BANK, PENNY...

CLIVE AND ALEX'S TEAM HAVE GOT TO DO A WEEK OF INTERNATIONAL PRESENTATIONS WITH A PUNISHING SCHEDULE OF SEVEN EUROPEAN CITIES IN FIVE DAYS...

A TRIP LIKE THIS CAN BRING SUCH OBVIOUS BENEFITS BUT THE BANK SEEMS TO HAVE NO QUALMS ABOUT CONSIGNING PEOPLE TO THE SQUALID DISCOMFORT OF ECONOMY CLASS...

ALEX AND CLIVE?

NO. YOU AND ME WHEN WE GO ON OUR SUMMER HOLIDAY...

OH MY GOD. THE BANK'S FLYING ALEX AND CLIVE EVERYWHERE BY PRIVATE JET...

EXACTLY. WHICH MEANS NO AIR MILES FOR THEM...

Strip 3:

LET'S SEE. SIR NIGEL SEDGEWICK. HOBBIES: OPERA, FISHING... WIFE'S NAME: DEBORAH...

I KEEP THESE CRIB SHEETS ON ALL SENIOR BUSINESS FIGURES AND I ALWAYS MUG UP ON THEIR PERSONAL DETAILS BEFORE CALLING...

HOW LAUGHABLY NAIVE, CLIVE...

LOOK, ALEX, IF YOU WANT TO BRING IN CORPORATE BUSINESS IT'S IMPORTANT TO STRIKE UP A PERSONAL RAPPORT WITH THE PEOPLE WHO WIELD THE POWER WITHIN A COMPANY....

PRECISELY... HERE.

SECRETARY: SHELLEY. HOBBIES: KARAOKE, KICK-BOXING...CAT'S NAME: TOFFEE...

FIRST YOU HAVE TO GET PUT THROUGH TO SIR NIGEL...

Strip 4:

NOW, TAKE SIMON OVER THERE. THERE'S AN INTERNET ENTREPRENEUR WHO I ACTUALLY ADMIRE...

HE STARTED UP A YEAR AGO, BUT UNLIKE MANY OTHERS HE HASN'T HYPOCRITICALLY WAVERED FROM HIS PRINCIPLES SINCE THE DOTCOM MARKETS TURNED DOWN.

IN THE FACE OF ADVERSITY HE'S KEPT FAITH WITH THE VISION THAT INSPIRED HIM, ALL OF WHICH CAN BE SEEN CLEARLY IN HIS COMMITMENT TO HIS BUSINESS...

REALLY?

YES. HE'S JACKED IT ALL IN NOW THERE'S NO CHANCE OF BECOMING AN INSTANT MULTI-MILLIONAIRE.

AH YES. SOMEONE WHO'S HONEST ABOUT BEING MOTIVATED BY PURE GREED...

Row 1:

STEVE REDGRAVE'S HISTORIC FIFTH GOLD MEDAL IS STILL A BIG TALKING POINT IN ALL CITY WINE BARS...

AMAZING VICTORY... ...JUST HELD OFF THE ITALIANS...

WHAT A HEROIC FEAT, REQUIRING COMMITMENT, MENTAL DISCIPLINE, TOTAL SELF-BELIEF AND AN UTTERLY POSITIVE ATTITUDE.

FOR ME THIS IS SOMETHING THAT EMBODIES THE TRUE MODERN-DAY SPIRIT OF WHAT IT IS TO BE BRITISH.

HAVING TO PRETEND TO CARE ABOUT MINORITY SPORTS BECAUSE WE'RE USELESS AT ALL THE PROPER ONES...

EXACTLY. LAST WEEK EVERYONE WAS ENTHUSING ABOUT DOUBLE TRAP SHOOTING...

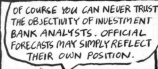

Row 2:

ALL OUR CHAPS ARE PATRIOTIC AND ITS ONLY NATURAL FOR THEM TO ENTHUSE ABOUT BRITISH OLYMPIC SUCCESSES...

OF COURSE MANY OF THE DISCIPLINES CONCERNED ARE MINORITY ONES LIKE SLALOM CANOEING BUT WE SHOULDN'T DISPARAGE THE EFFORTS OF THE PEOPLE CONCERNED.

AFTER ALL WE ARE WATCHING INDIVIDUALS WHO ARE DEMONSTRATING AN EXEMPLARY PROFESSIONALISM WITHIN THEIR CHOSEN FIELD.

STOCK-BROKING?

EXACTLY. BECOMING AN INSTANT EXPERT ON SOMETHING THEY KNOW NOTHING ABOUT. IT'S JUST LIKE THEIR JOBS...

...OUR WOMEN'S COXLESS FOURS... BIG CALLS... STROKE TO 37... BLAH BLAH...

Row 3:

OUR NEW ANALYST IS PREDICTING A BIG STOCK MARKET CRASH...

THERE'S ALWAYS TALK OF THAT AT THIS TIME OF YEAR.

OF COURSE YOU CAN NEVER TRUST THE OBJECTIVITY OF INVESTMENT BANK ANALYSTS. OFFICIAL FORECASTS MAY SIMPLY REFLECT THEIR OWN POSITION.

MEANING THE BANK'S GONE SHORT ON EQUITIES AND THUS WOULD BENEFIT FINANCIALLY FROM A DOWNTURN IN THE MARKET?

NO, THE ANALYST'S JUST SIGNED A NEW CONTRACT AND WOULD RATHER EVERYTHING WENT BELLY-UP NOW WHILE HE'S ON A TWO-YEAR GUARANTEED BONUS...

Row 4:

THIS IS THE TIME OF YEAR WHEN I START GETTING EXCITED ABOUT MY BONUS AND PLANNING HOW TO SPEND IT...

LOOK, ALEX, BOYS WILL BE BOYS, BUT COULD YOU BE MORE RESPONSIBLE THIS YEAR AND NOT BLOW A LOAD OF MONEY ON SOME SHORT TERM STATUS SYMBOL JUST BECAUSE YOUR MATES OWN ONE?

SOMETHING THAT DEPRECIATES SO RAPIDLY IN VALUE THAT IT'S WORTH LESS THAN HALF WHAT YOU PAID FOR IT WHEN YOU WANT TO SELL IT SIX MONTHS LATER...

DON'T WORRY, PENNY...

I WON'T BE INVESTING IN ANY DOT-COM START-UPS THIS YEAR... NOW WHERE'S THAT PORSCHE CATALOGUE?

THAT'S MORE LIKE IT...!

email: alex-cartoon@etgate.co.uk

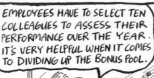

99

Alex PEATTIE + TAYLOR

IT'S ALWAYS NICE TO COME UP TO EDINBURGH UNIVERSITY FOR THE MILK ROUND.

YES INDEED, CLIVE.

THESE BRIGHT, EAGER, HARD-WORKING AMBITIOUS STUDENTS SEEM GRATEFUL THAT WE'RE HERE TO TALK TO THEM ABOUT CAREERS IN THE CITY...

IT'S FLATTERING THAT THEY OBVIOUSLY SEE US AS MENTORS AND ROLE-MODELS WHO EMBODY THE DEDICATION AND PROFESSIONALISM THEY ASPIRE TO.

YOUNG FOOLS. WE ONLY COME UP HERE BECAUSE IT'S A LONG WAY FROM LONDON, SO WE GET A WHOLE DAY OFF WORK...

AND THE BRAINY KIDS AT OXFORD AND CAMBRIDGE ASK TOUGH QUESTIONS WE CAN'T ANSWER...

Alex PEATTIE + TAYLOR

ALEX, DID I HEAR YOU SAY THAT YOU ONLY DO THE MILK ROUND BECAUSE IT'S A FREEBIE DAY OFF WORK AND YOU GET TO DRINK AT THE BANK'S EXPENSE?

BROADLY SPEAKING, YES, ROBIN.

I REALLY FAIL TO UNDERSTAND YOUR GENERATION. YOU'RE SO UNLIKE TODAY'S KEEN, AMBITIOUS, HARD-WORKING STUDENT...

IT SEEMS TO ME THAT YOU LOT BUMMED AROUND AT UNIVERSITY GIVING NO THOUGHT TO YOUR FUTURE OR JOB OPPORTUNITIES. I BET YOU NEVER EVEN WENT TO THE CAREERS FAIR...

OF COURSE I DID, ROBIN...

IT WAS A FREEBIE DAY OFF LECTURES AND WE GOT TO DRINK AT VARIOUS BANKS' EXPENSE...

Alex PEATTIE + TAYLOR

SO YOU GOT TIM TO DO THE PRESENTATION TO THE MILK ROUND STUDENTS?

THAT'S RIGHT, CLIVE.

IT OFFERS AN OPPORTUNITY FOR BRIGHT INQUIRING YOUNG MINDS TO QUIZ OUR PEOPLE ON ALL ELEMENTS OF MODERN BANKING...

PROVIDING A CONVENIENT FORUM FOR GATHERING PRACTICAL INFORMATION THAT MIGHT OTHERWISE BE DIFFICULT TO ASCERTAIN...

SO HOW MUCH DO YOU EARN?

AH...

ER....

CAREERS AT MEGA-BANK

HERE WE GO... I'VE ALWAYS WANTED TO FIND THIS OUT...

NUDGE

Alex PEATTIE + TAYLOR

OBVIOUSLY WE PAY OUT BONUSES TO REWARD OUR STAFF AND ALSO TO ENSURE WE DON'T LOSE THEM...

WHICH IS WHY WE HAVE NO HESITATION IN AWARDING ALEX A BONUS WHICH IS COLOSSAL BY MOST PEOPLE'S STANDARDS...

HE'S A TOP FEE GENERATOR FOR THE BANK AND WITHIN THE REALM OF FINANCE HE HAS CONSISTENTLY SHOWN THAT HE POSSESSES ALL THE QUALITIES WE LOOK FOR...

UTTERLY AND RECKLESSLY SPENDTHRIFT? YES, HE'LL HAVE BLOWN HIS BONUS BY FEBRUARY AS USUAL...

GOD FORBID HE SHOULD SQUIRREL IT ALL AWAY AND BE ABLE TO AFFORD TO RETIRE...

email: alex-cartoon@etgate.co.uk

2001

Strip 1:

I'M VERY PLEASED THAT OUR ORGANISATION HAS FINALLY MOVED WITH THE TIMES AND ADOPTED A PERMANENT DRESS-DOWN POLICY...

AFTER ALL THERE'S NO REASON WHY ANYONE SHOULD HAVE TO WEAR A SUIT TO THE OFFICE UNLESS THEY HAVE FORMAL MEETINGS TO ATTEND THAT DAY...

PERSONALLY I FIND THE NEW DRESS CODE HELPS ME COME INTO WORK FEELING RELAXED, CONFIDENT AND GOOD ABOUT MYSELF...

ER.... BUT YOU'RE WEARING A SUIT...

EXACTLY. AND AS I'M HEAD OF HUMAN RESOURCES THAT FACT STRIKES TERROR INTO THE HEART OF EVERYONE I MEET...

OH MY GOD HE'S SACKING PEOPLE TODAY...

email: alex-cartoon@etgate.co.uk

Strip 2:

SO WHAT HAPPENED TO ALEX YESTERDAY?

OH HE JUST POPPED OUT FOR A QUICK DRINK AFTER WORK WITH SOME OF THE TRADERS...

THEY ENDED UP GOING ON FOR A MEAL, MORE DRINKS, A COUPLE OF SLEAZY NIGHTCLUBS. THEN BY 4.30AM THERE WAS NO POINT IN GOING HOME SO HE CRASHED THE NIGHT IN THE OFFICE...

YOU'D NEVER GUESS THAT TO LOOK AT HIM NOW...

NO, BUT ALEX IS AN OLD HAND AT THIS GAME. YOU WON'T CATCH HIM SLUMPED UNSHAVEN AT HIS DESK WITH A BLEARY-EYED HANGOVER IN YESTERDAY'S SUIT... LIKE, ALEX ALWAYS KEEPS A FRESH SET OF CLOTHES IN THE OFFICE...

OH RIGHT...

YOU MEAN THE CRUMPLED DINNER JACKET AND BLACK TIE?

YES. SOMEHOW IT IMPARTS MORE DIGNITY.

ZZZZZ

email: alex-cartoon@etgate.co.uk

Strip 3:

SORRY TO HEAR YOU WERE BURGLED, TOBY. DID YOU LOSE MUCH?

SOME PAINTINGS, MY WIFE'S JEWELLERY...

ALL INSURED OBVIOUSLY, BUT IT'S REALLY BROUGHT HOME TO ME HOW I HAD FAILED TO TAKE CERTAIN ELEMENTARY HOUSEHOLD SECURITY PRECAUTIONS

IT'S NO FUN BEING BURGLED BUT THANKFULLY I'M NOW IN A POSITION TO BE ABLE TO PASS ON SOME VALUABLE PREVENTATIONAL ADVICE TO OTHERS...

SO THE POLICE THINK IT WAS ONE OF THOSE "WHO'S WHO" BURGLARIES...

YES. I MUST REMEMBER TO LIST MY CLUB RATHER THAN HOME ADDRESS IN NEXT YEAR'S EDITION..

DO STOP SHOWING OFF, DARLING...

CHAIRMAN

email: alex-cartoon@etgate.co.uk

Strip 4:

ALEX, YOU KNOW OUR GRADUATE TRAINEE WAS SUPPOSED TO BE TRAVELLING WITH US IN BUSINESS CLASS...

SO HE COULD BRIEF US EN ROUTE... OH, YES.. WHERE IS HE?

ER... I'VE GOT A TERRIBLE FEELING I GAVE HIM TOO MUCH PREPARATORY WORK TO DO. I KNOW HE WAS VERY LATE SETTING OFF FOR THE AIRPORT. I'M AFRAID WE MUST ASSUME THE WORST.

WHAT?

YOU USELESS BUNGLING IMBECILE, CLIVE. DO YOU REALISE WHAT YOU'VE DONE?

I'VE JUST BEEN HOPING THERE MIGHT BE SOME INNOCENT EXPLANATION FOR HIS NOT BEING HERE WITH US...

...LIKE THAT HE'D MISSED THE FLIGHT..

YOU MEAN HE ARRIVED SO LATE THAT BUSINESS CLASS WAS FULL SO THEY UPGRADED HIM TO FIRST?! I'LL NEVER LIVE THIS DOWN..

FIRST CLASS

Alex PEATTIE + TAYLOR

THERE ARE OTHER FACTORS TO BE CONSIDERED THESE DAYS BY A NEW EMPLOYEE OTHER THAN JUST SALARY AND PERKS, ROBIN.

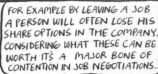

FOR EXAMPLE BY LEAVING A JOB A PERSON WILL OFTEN LOSE HIS SHARE OPTIONS IN THE COMPANY. CONSIDERING WHAT THESE CAN BE WORTH IT'S A MAJOR BONE OF CONTENTION IN JOB NEGOTIATIONS...

NOWADAYS IT'S COMMON TO FIND THERE IS AN INSISTENCE THAT THE NEW EMPLOYER COMPENSATATE THE CANDIDATE IN FULL FOR ANY LOST SHARE OPTIONS

NO NO... I INSIST... SO YOU HAD 10,000 SHARES IN THAT DOTCOM START-UP WORTH £37·18 EACH AT THEIR PEAK... VALUE OF STAKE AT TODAY'S PRICES...SHALL WE CALL IT A ROUND £200?

PLEASE CAN WE CHANGE THE SUBJECT?

Alex PEATTIE + TAYLOR

YOU REMEMBER MIKE, MR HARDCASTLE? HE'LL BE REJOINING THE TEAM ADVISING YOUR COMPANY...

AND WHERE'S HE BEEN?

I TOOK A SABBATICAL YEAR OUT, MR HARDCASTLE, IN WHICH I TRAVELLED ROUND INDIA AND SOUTH AMERICA... ER... BASICALLY TRYING TO, ER, "FIND MYSELF".

QUOTE QUOTE

PAH!

TYPICAL OF YOU NAMBY-PAMBY COLLEGE BOYS. I PAY YOU FEES BUT NOT ONE OF YOU'VE GOT THE FIRST CLUE ABOUT THE REAL WORLD OR HOW TO RUN A PROPER HANDS-ON BUSINESS...

IT'D HAVE BEEN MUCH WORSE IF YOU'D TOLD HIM THE TRUTH, MIKE...

THAT I SET UP A DOTCOM THAT WENT BUST? YES, I KNOW...

Alex PEATTIE + TAYLOR

THE WHOLE FACE OF THE CITY OF LONDON IS CHANGING DUE TO THE DRESS-DOWN REVOLUTION...

YOUR AVERAGE OFFICE IS A SARTORIAL NIGHTMARE THANKS TO THE YANKS...

AGREED, CLIVE. BUT LET'S NOT FORGET THE BENEFITS THE AMERICANS HAVE BROUGHT US...

FOR EXAMPLE THEIR DISCIPLINED WORK ETHIC AND TOTAL COMMITMENT TO BUSINESS EXCELLENCE WHICH HAVE PRODUCED THE MOST COMMENDABLE RESULTS.

EH?

NAMELY THAT NONE OF THEM ARE ALLOWED OUT TO LUNCH TO SULLY THE TONE OF PLACES LIKE THIS WITH THEIR GHASTLY CHINOS...

THANK GOODNESS...

Alex PEATTIE + TAYLOR

LOOK AT CLIVE STANDING IN THE CORRIDOR TALKING ON HIS MOBILE.

YES. I'VE SEEN HIM DOING THAT ON A NUMBER OF OCCASIONS...

DID YOU NOTICE HOW FURTIVE AND EMBARRASSED HE LOOKED?

YES. PRESUMABLY HE'S TALKING TO A HEADHUNTER OR DEALING IN INSIDE INFORMATION...

AS YOU SAY, CLEARLY SOME MATTER WHICH PREVENTS HIM FROM BEING ABLE TO USE HIS OFFICE FACILITIES AS NORMAL...

WE'D BETTER KEEP A CLOSE EYE ON HIM IN FUTURE...

AGREED...

ALL RIGHT, CLIVE, I'M ON TO IT...

COULD SOMEONE OPEN THE DOOR FOR CLIVE? HE FORGOT HIS SECURITY PASS WHEN HE WENT TO THE LOO AS USUAL...

Alex PEATTIE + TAYLOR

THE POSSIBLE U.S. RECESSION WILL PROBABLY BE ONLY SHORT-LIVED BUT IT LEAVES COMPANIES IN AN AWKWARD SITUATION...

OBVIOUSLY THERE'S A TEMPTATION TO PANIC AND REDUCE HEADCOUNT, BUT THE LIKELIHOOD IS THAT IT WILL BE NECESSARY TO RE-HIRE THE PEOPLE IN 6 MONTHS WHEN THINGS PICK UP AGAIN...

HMM...YES...

MOST OF OUR RIVALS SEEM TO HAVE GONE FOR THIS SHORT-TERMIST KNEE-JERK OPTION

WHICH PRESENTS US WITH A CLEAR-CUT POSITIVE OPPORTUNITY.

TO FOLLOW SUIT?

PRECISELY. SO LET'S SACK LOTS OF PEOPLE. YOU NEVER LOOK STUPID FOR HAVING DONE EXACTLY THE SAME AS EVERYONE ELSE...

email: alex-cartoon@etgate.co.uk

Alex PEATTIE + TAYLOR

CLIVE, DID YOU DO THAT VALUATION OF HAPPYBANG.COM FOR RUPERT SO THAT WE CAN SELL IT OFF?

YES, ALEX...

THE COMPANY HAS NO PRODUCT, NO ASSETS AND NO STAFF. IT'S VALUE IS THEREFORE ZILLH.

BUT, CLIVE, IT RECEIVED £100M IN FUNDING LAST YEAR...

EXACTLY, ALEX, AND THE 23-YEAR-OLD DIRECTORS BLEW THE LOT OF IT ON LIVING THE LIFE OF RILEY AND FLYING THEMSELVES FIRST CLASS ALL OVER THE WORLD...

HMM...

"HAPPYBANG.COM: TOTAL VALUATION: £500,000..."

THAT'S WHAT WE RECKON THEIR AIR MILES ARE WORTH...

email: alex-cartoon@etgate.co.uk

Alex PEATTIE + TAYLOR

LOOK, ALEX, LAST YEAR, ON YOUR ADVICE MY COMPANY SPENT MILLIONS ESTABLISHING AN "INTERNET PRESENCE"...

SINCE THEN THE DOTCOM THING HAS GONE BELLY-UP AND WE'RE NOW GOING TO HAVE TO MAKE AN ANNOUNCEMENT THAT WE'RE WRITING OFF THE ENTIRE INVESTMENT... MY SHARE PRICE WILL BE CRUCIFIED.

THIS IS YOUR FAULT, ALEX. YOU TOLD ME THAT THE INTERNET WOULD PROVIDE ME WITH BUSINESS SOLUTIONS...

AND SO IT WILL, MR HARDCASTLE...

WE'LL POST THE ANNOUNCEMENT ON YOUR WEBSITE. ABSOLUTELY NOBODY WILL SEE IT THERE...

email: alex-cartoon@etgate.co.uk

Alex PEATTIE + TAYLOR

WE HAD A MARVELLOUS LONG WEEKEND SKIING. IT WAS THE FIRST TIME WE'VE BEEN AS A FAMILY...

OF COURSE JEREMY GOES ON HIS BANK'S CORPORATE SKIING TRIP EVERY YEAR. I'M PLEASED TO SAY THAT HIS COMPETENCE ON THE SKI SLOPES FINALLY SEEMS TO HAVE IMPROVED...

THIS IS THE FIRST TIME EVER THAT HE HASN'T COME BACK WITH AN ARM OR A LEG IN PLASTER... ISN'T IT, JEREMY?

HA HA...YES, DARLING. THAT'S RIGHT...

AHEM... NOT A WORD, PLEASE, ALEX...

WHAT, THAT ALL YOUR INJURIES ON PREVIOUS TRIPS WERE SUSTAINED WHILE STAGGERING BACK TO OUR HOTEL AT 4 A.M.?

email: alex-cartoon@etgate.co.uk

Alex PEATTIE + TAYLOR

AS YOU KNOW, ALEX, TODAY WE'RE BUILDING HOMES FOR POOR FAMILIES UNDER THE "HABITAT FOR HUMANITY" SCHEME.

NOW, THE CHOICE OF VEHICLE BY WHICH A HIGHLY-PAID INVESTMENT BANKER ARRIVES IN THIS UNDER-PRIVILEGED URBAN AREA IS AN ISSUE OF SOME DELICACY...

YOU ARE TO BE CONGRATULATED FOR REALISING THAT IT WOULD NOT BE APPROPRIATE TO CRUISE UP IN ONE'S EXPENSIVE CAR, SYMBOLISING WEALTH AND PRIVILEGE... OF COURSE.

SOME LOCAL RUFFIANS MIGHT HALF-INCH IT...

BUT I STILL THINK THE TAXI WITH THE METER RUNNING IS A TAD INSENSITIVE...

TICK TICK TICK

email: alex-cartoon@etgate.co.uk

Alex PEATTIE + TAYLOR

BUILDING HOUSES FOR UNDERPRIVILEGED FAMILIES UNDER THE HABITAT FOR HUMANITY SCHEME IS VERY THERAPEUTIC...

IT'S EASY FOR US TO BECOME COMPLACENT AND FORGET ABOUT EXISTENCES FAR REMOVED FROM YOUR AND MY MODERN, HI-TECH CONVENIENCE LIFESTYLES...

AN EXPERIENCE LIKE THIS IS A STARK REMINDER OF THE HEAVY BURDEN THAT LIFE CAN INFLICT ON CERTAIN UNFORTUNATE INDIVIDUALS...

I MEAN, THE MOBILE PHONES WE USED TO HAVE TO LUG AROUND IN THE EIGHTIES WERE ABOUT THIS SIZE.

I KNOW... PHEW... HOWEVER DID WE MANAGE?

email: alex-cartoon@etgate.co.uk

Alex PEATTIE + TAYLOR

THIS "HABITAT FOR HUMANITY" SCHEME GIVES INVESTMENT BANKERS THE CHANCE TO GIVE SOMETHING BACK TO THE COMMUNITY...

OUR EMPLOYER GENEROUSLY GIVES US THE DAY OFF WORK FOR US TO SPEND HELPING TO BUILD HOUSES FOR POOR AND NEEDY PEOPLE...

WE ONLY RECEIVE MINIMAL TRAINING BUT SOME OF US JUST SEEM TO TAKE TO IT. I MEAN LOOK AT ALEX. HE'S LIKE A PROFESSIONAL BUILDER ALREADY.

YES...

HE TURNED UP AT 10, WORKED FOR HALF AN HOUR, HIS MOBILE RANG AND NOW HE'S OFF TO DO A MORE IMPORTANT JOB...

WE'RE UNDER-WRITING THE IPO AT 145.

email: alex-cartoon@etgate.co.uk

Alex PEATTIE + TAYLOR

SOMETIMES RECRUITING A PERSON TO THE BANK CAN GIVE ONE A REAL SENSE OF FULFILMENT AND SATISFACTION...

ESPECIALLY WHEN ONE IS ABLE TO REWARD AN INDIVIDUAL FINANCIALLY FOR HIS INITIATIVE, JUDGEMENT AND ENTERPRISE...

FOR EXAMPLE I'VE JUST HIRED AN EXPERIENCED BANKER FOR A £30,000 PAY RISE ON THE SALARY HE WAS GETTING AT HIS LAST COMPANY...

YES...

AND IT'S STILL ONLY A QUARTER OF WHAT HE WAS EARNING HERE LAST YEAR...

SERVES THE IDIOT RIGHT FOR JOINING A DOTCOM AND GETTING PAID IN STOCK OPTIONS...

HEE HEE HEE

email: alex-cartoon@etgate.co.uk

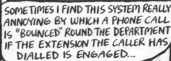

Alex PEATTIE + TAYLOR

YES... OKAY, I'VE GOT THAT... THANKS FOR CALLING... GOOD-BYE...

SOMETIMES I FIND THIS SYSTEM REALLY ANNOYING BY WHICH A PHONE CALL IS "BOUNCED" ROUND THE DEPARTMENT IF THE EXTENSION THE CALLER HAS DIALLED IS ENGAGED...

IF YOU HAPPEN NOT TO BE ON YOUR PHONE AT THE WRONG MOMENT YOU CAN END UP PICKING UP A CALL YOU'VE NO DESIRE TO TAKE.

WHO WAS IT?

MY CAR DEALER TELLING ME MY NEW PORSCHE IS READY FOR COLLECTION...

BAD LUCK. THAT'S ONE MESSAGE YOU'D REALLY WANT A COLLEAGUE TO TAKE FOR YOU...

email: alex-cartoon@etgate.co.uk

Alex PEATTIE + TAYLOR

HAVE YOU SEEN BEN PHILLIPS SINCE HE LEFT THE CITY TO RUN HIS OWN BUSINESS, CLIVE?

ER... WELL...

ACTUALLY I HAVE. TO BE HONEST, I APPLIED TO BE HIS FINANCE DIRECTOR. WELL, YOU KNOW WE'VE HAD NO BUSINESS HERE AT THE BANK FOR 6 MONTHS...

SO, WHAT HAPPENED?

I'M EMBARRASSED TO SAY HE TURNED ME DOWN FLAT. HE REALISED STRAIGHT AWAY HOW RUSTY I WAS... THAT I HADN'T LOOKED OVER A COMPANY REPORT AND ACCOUNTS FOR AGES...

HE HAD TO REMIND ME HOW LITTLE AN F.D. EARNS... OUR GRADUATE TRAINEE GETS MORE THAN THAT...

TRAGICALLY, YOU AND I COULD NEVER AFFORD TO WORK OUTSIDE THE CITY...

email: alex-cartoon@etgate.co.uk

Alex PEATTIE + TAYLOR

I SOMETIMES WORRY ABOUT THE DEMANDS THAT THE BANK'S WORK ETHIC PLACES ON ITS EMPLOYEES.

TAKE GILES. AT 35 HE'S ONE OF OUR TOP PEOPLE, HIGHLY-PAID AND MOTIVATED, BUT HE WORKS PUNISHINGLY LONG HOURS IN AN ENVIRONMENT WHICH IS STILL MALE-DOMINATED.

HE NEVER MEETS ANY WOMEN, CERTAINLY NEVER HAS A CHANCE TO FORM A RELATIONSHIP WITH ANY. IT'S VERY UNNATURAL AND COULD HAVE DISTURBING CONSEQUENCES...

YES...

...HE MIGHT STAY MARRIED AND BE PRESSURISED BY HIS WIFE INTO TAKING EARLY RETIREMENT...

QUITE, WHEREAS IF HE FOUND HIMSELF A MISTRESS AND THEN GOT DIVORCED HE WOULDN'T BE ABLE TO AFFORD TO RETIRE...

email: alex-cartoon@etgate.co.uk

Alex PEATTIE + TAYLOR

HELLO, IS THAT RUPERT STERLING? IT'S DAVID GRAVES HERE...

SORRY TO CALL YOU ON YOUR MOBILE BUT YOU KNOW HOW HARD IT CAN BE FOR US SENIOR PEOPLE TO GET TO TALK TO EACH OTHER...

MOBILE PHONES ARE THE BEST WAY OF GETTING THROUGH URGENTLY TO SOMEONE WHO COULD BE IN THE MOST INACCESSIBLE PLACE IN THE WORLD...

I'M IN MY OFFICE, YES...

HELLO, IT'S DAVID GRAVES' SECRETARY... I HAVE MR GRAVES FOR MR STERLING...

NO. YOU PUT YOUR BOSS ON THE LINE FIRST...

PUT HIM ON THE LINE PLEASE...

I'LL PUT MINE ON AFTER YOU PUT YOURS ON.

email: alex-cartoon@etgate.co.uk

Strip 1:

WITH AN ELECTION IMMINENT, CERTAIN POLITICIANS MUST BE LOOKING AT THE CITY WITH ALARM...

AFTER ALL WE ARE AN ADVANCE ECONOMIC INDICATOR AND CURRENTLY MARKETS ARE FALLING DOWN AND PEOPLE HERE ARE STARTING TO FEAR FOR THEIR JOBS... THAT'S TRUE.

I HARDLY NEED POINT OUT WHICH PARTY HAS THE MOST TO LOSE FROM THE COUNTRY ENTERING RECESSION JUST BEFORE A GENERAL ELECTION...

THE CONSERVATIVES... EXACTLY. RIGHT NOW NO ONE IN THE CITY WOULD DARE TAKE TIME OFF WORK TO STAND AS A CANDIDATE...

Strip 2:

I'M NEVER GOING TO A CONCERT WITH YOU AGAIN, CLIVE. I CAN'T BELIEVE YOU FORGOT TO SWITCH OFF YOUR MOBILE...

WHEN IT RANG LOUDLY HALF WAY THROUGH THE PERFORMANCE IT TOTALLY DESTROYED THE AESTHETIC EXPERIENCE FOR THE DISCRIMINATING MUSIC-LOVER...

OUR SOPHISTICATED EARS WERE SUBJECTED TO THE UGLY, TEETH-JARRING CLASH BETWEEN SHRILL, HARSH ELECTRONIC TONES AND AN ELEGANT CLASSICAL MELODY...

HIS RINGER PLAYED THE 1812 OVERTURE... HOW NAFF... IT COMPLETELY RUINED THAT HARRISON BIRTWHISTLE EXPERIMENTAL PIECE FOR ME... PHILISTINE!

PRE-ORDERED INTERVAL DRINKS COLLECTION POINT

email: alex-cartoon@etgate.co.uk

Strip 3:

YOU'RE SUCH A LUDDITE, ALEX. YOU REALLY SHOULD GET ONE OF THESE SLIM LIGHTWEIGHT TELEPHONE HEADSETS LIKE I HAVE...

IT ALLOWS ME TO SIT PERFECTLY NATURALLY AS I SPEAK ON THE PHONE, UNLIKE YOU WITH THAT OLD-FASHIONED CHUNKY RECEIVER CLAMPED TO YOUR HEAD.

LOOK AT THAT HUNCHED AWKWARD POSTURE IT FORCES YOU TO ADOPT. I TELL YOU, USING THAT THING COULD LEAD TO DAMAGING LONG-TERM CONSEQUENCES FOR YOU... YOU THINK SO, JONATHAN?

HAVE YOU NOTICED HOW JONATHAN NEVER SEEMS TO BE ON THE PHONE, UNLIKE ALEX? HMM... YES. ANOTHER CANDIDATE FOR THE REDUNDANCY LIST?

email: alex-cartoon@etgate.co.uk

Strip 4:

THIS FOOT AND MOUTH CRISIS HAS BEEN A BIT OF A NIGHTMARE EH? FAT LOT YOU TOWNIES CARE...

YOU'RE ALL SO INSULAR AND SHORT-SIGHTED ABOUT THIS EPIDEMIC... THE WAY YOU WORRY ABOUT IT CAUSING PROBLEMS WITH YOUR CORPORATE EVENTS LIKE RUGBY OR RACING OR PRECIOUS BLOODY GLYNDEBOURNE...

I BET NONE OF YOU'VE GIVEN A SECOND THOUGHT TO THE EFFECT IT MIGHT BE HAVING ON COWS, HAVE YOU? ON THE CONTRARY...

...I'M AS RELIEVED AS ANYONE ELSE THAT COWES IS UNLIKELY TO BE AFFECTED...

email: alex-cartoon@etgate.co.uk

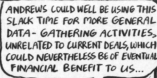

Strip 1

Alex PEATTIE + TAYLOR

I SEE YOU'VE PUT ANDREWS ON THE REDUNDANCY LIST. AREN'T YOU BEING A BIT HASTY? I MEAN HE ALWAYS LOOKS VERY BUSY...

RUPERT, IT'S EASY ENOUGH FOR A CHAP TO SIT STARING AT HIS COMPUTER SCREEN ALL DAY, BUT WE BOTH KNOW THE BANK'S GOT NO BUSINESS ON...

YOU SHOULD AT LEAST CHECK WITH THE I.T. DEPARTMENT...

ANDREWS COULD WELL BE USING THIS SLACK TIME FOR MORE GENERAL DATA-GATHERING ACTIVITIES, UNRELATED TO CURRENT DEALS, WHICH COULD NEVERTHELESS BE OF EVENTUAL FINANCIAL BENEFIT TO US...

WHAT, SUCH AS DOWNLOADING PORN OFF THE INTERNET? QUITE. IN WHICH CASE WE CAN SACK HIM AND NOT HAVE TO PAY HIM ANY REDUNDANCY MONEY.

email: alex-cartoon@etgate.co.uk

Strip 2

Alex PEATTIE + TAYLOR

THE DOWNTURN IN BUSINESS IS WORSE THAN EXPECTED. MOST OF OUR CHAPS ARE JUST TWIDDLING THEIR THUMBS.

OF COURSE IT'S GOOD NEWS FOR THOSE OF OUR ANALYSTS WHO ARE SITTING THEIR C.F.A. EXAMS ON SATURDAY. WITH ALL THIS EXTRA REVISION TIME THEY SHOULD ALL PASS... THAT'S TRUE.

AND IF THE BANK'S TO SURVIVE IN THIS DOG-EAT-DOG RECESSIONARY ENVIRONMENT ALL OUR ANALYSTS GAINING THIS IMPORTANT QUALIFICATION WILL BE A SIGNIFICANT FACTOR... YES...

...WE'LL HAVE TO PAY THEM ALL MORE MONEY... NIGHTMARE... I PROPOSE WE SEND THEM ON A 3-DAY OUTWARD BOUND COURSE TOMORROW TO GET THE PASS RATE DOWN...

email: alex-cartoon@etgate.co.uk

Strip 3

Alex PEATTIE + TAYLOR

THIS IS SO TYPICAL. WE'RE IN A BEAR MARKET AND WHO GETS SACKED? TRADERS, ANALYSTS... PEOPLE WHO MAKE MONEY FOR THE BANK...

YET THE MIDDLE OFFICE - ALL THE MARKETING AND CORPORATE COMMUNICATIONS PEOPLE - GET TO KEEP THEIR JOBS. WHY? WHAT DO THEY PRODUCE...?

I'LL TELL YOU: SPIN, FROTH, HOT AIR, MEANINGLESS VERBIAGE... SO HOW EXACTLY DOES THEIR CONTINUED EMPLOYMENT AT THE BANK CONTRIBUTE TO COST-SAVING? AH, YOU'D BE SURPRISED, CLIVE...

WELL, WE CAN'T AFFORD TO PAY OUT ANY MONEY THIS BONUS TIME. SO SOMEONE HAS TO THINK UP THE FANCY NEW JOB TITLES WE'LL FOB OUR PEOPLE OFF WITH... "DEPUTY ASSOCIATE EXECUTIVE DIRECTOR"

CORPORATE COMMUNICATIONS

"VICE GLOBAL OPERATIONS STRATEGIST"

email: alex-cartoon@etgate.co.uk

Strip 4

Alex PEATTIE + TAYLOR

WHAT DOES THAT STICKER ON ALEX'S CAR SAY? "ECOLOGY WARNING. STOP THESE OUTSIZE VEHICLES"

THOSE STICKERS HAVE BEEN APPEARING ON LOTS OF BIG FUEL-INEFFICIENT CARS IN THE AREA... AND THEY'RE INCREDIBLY DIFFICULT TO PEEL OFF WITHOUT DAMAGING THE PAINTWORK... OH. HOW ANNOYING!

WELL OBVIOUSLY THE USE OF MACHINES THAT CONTRIBUTE TO GLOBAL WARMING SHOULD NOT BE ENCOURAGED. I THINK CERTAIN PEOPLE NEED TO GET THE MESSAGE... CAR OWNERS?

NO, ENVIRONMENTAL ACTIVISTS. THE ONLY WAY TO GET THE STICKERS OFF IS TO MELT THE GLUE WITH A HAIR DRYER...

email: alex-cartoon@etgate.co.uk

Strip 1:

WE'VE OFFERED ALL THIS YEAR'S GRADUATE INTAKE £15,000 TO TAKE A GAP YEAR TO PURSUE A PROJECT OF THEIR CHOICE...

NOT ONLY DOES THIS POLICY SHOW THAT WE'RE A CARING EMPLOYER BUT IT WILL ALSO GIVE US AN IDEA OF THE CALIBRE OF THE PEOPLE WE'VE RECRUITED.

IT'S ALL VERY WELL HAVING A UNIVERSITY DEGREE BUT WILL THEY BE ABLE TO DEMONSTRATE THAT THEY HAVE A REAL HANDS-ON UNDERSTANDING OF THE WAY THE BUSINESS WORLD WORKS...?

I HEAR THAT TEN OF THEM HAVE ACCEPTED...

THAT'S RIGHT...

SO CLEARLY THEY CAN'T SEE THAT THIS IS A BLATANT PLOY TO GET HEADCOUNT DOWN IN A RECESSION...

LITTLE FOOLS. WE'LL MAKE SURE NONE OF THEM HAS A JOB TO COME BACK TO...

Strip 2:

I CAN'T BELIEVE IT, ALEX. MY WIFE JUST ASKED ME FOR A DIVORCE. IT CAME RIGHT OUT OF THE BLUE

AFTER TEN YEARS TOGETHER...WITH NO OBVIOUS PROBLEMS...SHE SAYS SHE'S JUST FALLEN OUT OF LOVE WITH ME. HOW COULD SHE DO THIS?

WHY DIDN'T SHE TALK TO ME ABOUT IT EARLIER? WHY DIDN'T I SEE IT COMING? I COULD HAVE ACTED DIFFERENTLY... DONE SOMETHING ABOUT THE SITUATION... AND NOW IT'S TOO LATE...

NO... NO, IT'S NOT...

WHAT? YOU THINK I CAN STILL GET TICKETS TO GO TO AUSTRALIA TO SEE THE BRITISH LIONS TOUR AT SUCH SHORT NOTICE?

WELL, IT'S WORTH A TRY...

Strip 3:

THIS WHOLE ELECTION AND PRE-ELECTION PERIOD HAS BEEN CHARACTERISED BY APATHY BOREDOM AND CYNICISM...

YEAH.

LABOUR HAS HANDLED THE ECONOMY BETTER THAN ANTICIPATED BUT MARKETS HAVE TAKEN A DECIDED TURN FOR THE WORSE THIS YEAR... BUT IN THE END, WHAT CAN ONE DO ABOUT IT?

SO WHEN I THOUGHT ABOUT GOING DOWN TO THE POLLING STATION BEFORE COMING INTO WORK TODAY I'M AFRAID APATHY TOOK OVER...

OH NO... YOU MEAN...?

YOU VOTED?...BUT NO INVESTMENT BANKER EVER ADMITS TO BEING AVAILABLE BETWEEN 7AM AND 10 P.M....

CLIVE, WE'VE GOT NO WORK ON AND I DON'T CARE WHO KNOWS IT...

YAWN

Strip 4:

WHEN ONE HEARS THAT AN EMPLOYEE HAS BEEN TRYING TO GET HIMSELF A NEW JOB IT CAN COME AS A RELIEF...

IN A BEAR MARKET WHERE WE'VE GOT TO GET HEADCOUNT DOWN, ONE'S ALWAYS HALF-HOPING THAT PEOPLE WILL RESIGN AND SAVE US HAVING TO PAY OUT REDUNDANCY MONEY...

FOR EXAMPLE, HENDERSON WENT UP FOR A JOB WITH A FOUR-YEAR GUARANTEE...

WHO CAN BLAME HIM? IT'S VERY RARE TO GET THAT LEVEL OF JOB SECURITY IN THE MODERN CITY...

...SADLY IT WAS CONSERVATIVE CANDIDATE FOR RHYDDLYNNEN EAST...

I'LL MAKE SURE HIS SECURITY PASS IS CANCELLED BEFORE HE GETS BACK ON MONDAY...

Alex PEATTIE + TAYLOR

 BUSINESS HAS BEEN SO QUIET OVER RECENT MONTHS IT'S MARVELLOUS TO SEE OUR DEALING ROOM BUSY AGAIN...

 TRADERS BUYING AND SELLING POSITIONS, THE AGONY WHEN SOMEONE LOSES A LOT OF MONEY, THE ECSTASY WHEN HE CALLS THE MARKET RIGHT AND MAKES A SHEDLOAD...

 ALL USING THAT CUNNING BLEND OF INFORMED JUDGEMENT AND MARKET SAVVY THAT CHARACTERISES THE CITY TRADER.

BUT, ALEX, IT'S SUMMER: THE DEAD SEASON IN A DEAD YEAR...

 EXACTLY. WITH ASCOT, WIMBLEDON, THE LIONS TOUR AND THE ASHES, SPREAD BETTING'S NEVER BEEN BUSIER...

BUY WARNE NO-BALLS...

SELL RUDEDSKI ACES...

BUY AUSSIE PUNCHES...

Alex PEATTIE + TAYLOR

 WITH THE BONUS OUTLOOK BLEAK THE DEPARTMENT IS INVISIBLY DIVIDED INTO THE "HAVES" AND "HAVE-NOTS", ROBIN...

 THOSE WHO ARE ON GUARANTEED BONUSES AND THOSE WHO HAVE TO GENERATE SOME CLIENT INCOME IN ORDER TO SEE ANY FINANCIAL REWARD AT THE END OF THE YEAR. OBVIOUSLY A CERTAIN INDOLENCE DEVELOPS IN ONE GROUP...

 WITH BUSINESS IMPOSSIBLE TO COME BY ANYWAY THEY HAVE VERY LITTLE INCENTIVE TO EXERT THEMSELVES— AFTER ALL ITS NOT GOING TO AFFECT THEIR YEAR END REMUNERATION...

THOSE ON GUARANTEES?

 NO, THE REST OF US ON DIDDLY-SQUAT. WHY PUT THE MONEY IN THE BONUS POOL JUST SO THE BANK CAN HONOUR ITS PLEDGES AND GIVE IT TO THE OTHERS...?

Alex PEATTIE + TAYLOR

 "MEGABANK IS A GLOBALLY POSITIONED MARKET LEADER AND EMPLOYER OF CHOICE." WHY IS RUPERT E-MAILING US THIS CORPORATE GUFF?

 IT'S A CODED WARNING, CLIVE. WE ALL KNOW THAT BUSINESS HAS BEEN DIRE OF LATE. RUPERT IS SUBTLY TELLING US NOT TO EXPECT A BONUS THIS YEAR.

OH GOD. DO YOU THINK SO?

 UNDOUBTEDLY. THIS E-MAIL IS DESIGNED TO ENCOURAGE US TO ACCENTUATE THE POSITIVE:- TO BE GRATEFUL FOR WHAT WE HAVE - I.E.:- A JOB HERE- RATHER THAN HANKER AFTER FURTHER REWARDS.

I SEE...

 THIS IS A REALLY GREAT LITTLE CAR OF YOURS, BRIDGET. SO COMPACT AND RELIABLE AND IT HANDLES REALLY WELL...

WHAT ARE YOU TRYING TO TELL ME, CLIVE?

Alex PEATTIE + TAYLOR

 YOU'VE GOT TO REMEMBER, ROBIN, THAT THE CITY IS ALWAYS LOOKING A YEAR OR SO BEYOND CURRENT EVENTS...

 FOR EXAMPLE, THE U.S. ECONOMY SLOWS DOWN, FOLLOWED BY EUROPE, BUT WE'VE ALREADY FORESEEN THESE EVENTUALITIES AND FACTORED THEM INTO THE STOCK MARKET BEFORE THEY'VE HAPPENED...

I SEE...

 SO, ALEX, THE FACT THAT YOU'RE NOW LOOKING OPPORTUNITIES IN THE FAR EASTERN MARKETS INDICATES THAT THE PACIFIC RIM WILL BE A SIGNIFICANT AREA OF OPERATIONS A YEAR DOWN THE LINE...

PRECISELY, ROBIN...

 JAPAN AND KOREA ARE HOSTING THE WORLD CUP, SO IT'S VITAL I START ACTIVATING CONTACTS OUT THERE IF I'M GOING TO GET TO ANY OF THE MATCHES...

ALEX ORIGINALS AND PRINTS

The ALEX cartoon strip originals are all for sale. A strip measures 4 x 14 inches. If there's a particular one you want, phone or fax us some information about it (the date it appeared, what the punch line was etc.) and we'll let you know if we've still got it. If the original is not available, or you are too mean to purchase it, we can make a print of it for you. Originals and prints are signed by both Peattie and Taylor.

For further details on prices and delivery please call 01371 831846. T-shirts and calendars are also available.

ALEX BOOKS

Here for the first time, Alex shares some of the tricks that have kept him at the top in the world of international finance.

Alex dispenses tips on how to massage your cv, lie your way successfully through a job interview, survive the humiliations of your first year as a graduate trainee, blag your boss into giving you a bigger bonus and finally get yourself headhunted to a better job.

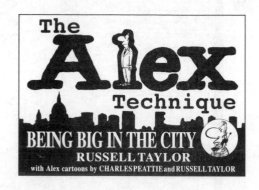

Also available: Alex III Son of Alex (1990), Alex Plays the Game (1994) and Alex Sweeps the Board (1996).

Originals, prints and books are available from:
Alex
Orchard End
Watling Lane
Thaxted
Dunmow
CM6 2QY

Tel. 01371 831846
Fax. 01371 831847
Email alex-cartoon@etgate.co.uk

PLEASE LOOK OUT FOR THE ALEX WEBSITE IN 2002 - www. alexcartoon.com

Also by the creators of Alex:
The Looniness of the Long Distance Runner by Russell Taylor (Andre Deutsch £16.99) A humorous account of an unfit Londoner's attempt to run the New York City Marathon from scratch.

All authors royalties from this book will be donated to National Missing Persons Helpline (registered charity No 1020419)